Lucifer
Over
London

Published by Influx Press
The Greenhouse
49 Green Lanes, London, N16 9BU
www.influxpress.com / @InfluxPress
All rights reserved.
© Saleh Addonia, Chloe Aridjis, Vanni Bianconi, Viola di Grado, Xiaolu
Guo, Susana Moreira Marques, Joanna Walsh, Zinovy Zinik, Wolfgang
Lehrner.

Copyright of the text rests with the authors.
The rights of Saleh Addonia, Chloe Aridjis, Vanni Bianconi, Viola di
Grado, Xiaolu Guo, Susana Moreira Marques, Joanna Walsh, Zinovy
Zinik, Wolfgang Lehrner to be identified as the authors of this work has
been asserted in accordance with section 77 of the Copyright, Designs and
Patents Act 1988.

First published in Italian by Humboldt Books, 2018

This book is in copyright. Subject to statutory exception and to provisions
of relevant collective licensing agreements, no reproduction of any part
may take place without the written permission of Influx Press.

This edition 2020. Printed and bound in the UK by TJ Books.

Paperback ISBN: 9781910312391
Ebook ISBN: 9781910312407

Cover design: Austin Burke
Interior design: Vince Haig
Proofreader: Trudi Shaw

This book is sold subject to the condition that it shall not, by way of trade
or otherwise, be lent, re-sold, hired out, or otherwise circulated without
the publisher's prior consent in any form of binding or cover other than
that in which it is published and without a similar condition including this
condition being imposed on the subsequent purchaser.

Contents

Oath to the Queen
Xiaolu Guo

1.

Once I saw a newsreel of Queen Elizabeth II making a speech when I was still living in Beijing in the 1990s. I was puzzled by the way she spoke English, even though I could not understand half of what she said. I noticed that her lips barely moved when she spoke. She seemed to have the quality of a ventriloquist, but there was no little painted doll sitting on her shoulder flapping its lips. Her whole manner was strange and impenetrable. I never got to the bottom of my puzzlement. A few years later, however, after managing to get a scholarship, I came to Britain, and started to live in London. Then began a journey of discovering English and Englishness.

For the first few years in London, I struggled to understand the language of the BBC and newspapers articles. This language was very different from the everyday language I had got to know in the street and on buses. It was full of political vocabulary and journalistic conventions that I found opaque and remote. Watching the Queen's speech now regularly on television gave me no encouragement either. So

I went back to my usual habit: studying words from English menus in eateries. One day, as I was having breakfast in my local café, I heard a tune from the radio, which blasted from speakers on the ceiling. The middle-aged lady who served tea shouted to a chef near the counter: '*The Archers*! Can you turn it up, Jim!'. 'Sure, Dot!' was the reply.

Then suddenly the café reverberated with a jingle-jangly jaunty theme tune. When that died away, some English voices started to resound. I listened with anticipation trying to discern the point of it. It deduced that it was a soap drama, composed by interminable dialogues between elderly English characters in a rural country setting. There was the occasional moo of a cow, baa of a sheep, and the sound of machinery. The characters spoke *English* English, definitely not foreigners' English. The lady in the cafe, Dot, leaning by the counter listened with mild concentration while folding napkins with a beatific smile. I thought this program must be of some national importance, since no one in the café complained about the noise. I listened attentively till it finished, by then I had deposited the baked beans and white toast in my oriental stomach. Then the news started. Dot, looking a little flushed, turned the sound down. She didn't seem to care about news or world affairs. An atmosphere of relative peace and quietness returned to the café, which gave me a chance to ask Dot some questions when she came to clear my table.

'The programme you just listened to, is it very important?' I asked with my broken English.

'You mean *the Archers*, love? You ain't never heard of it?!' She looked unbelievingly at me, as if I had only recently emerged from the jungle, a total ignoramus about worldly things. 'Don't you know 5 million people in this country listen to it every day?!' Dot wiped my table with vigor and pride.

'Oh, really!' I was impressed. 'What is it about? I come from China…' I inserted my question apologetically.

'You come from China! You're new then?' The lady re-arranged the mustard jar on the table and wiped the ketchup bottle with a rag. 'It's about family life on a farm in the Midlands. You know, we English like these sorts of settings – sheep, cows, dairy farming, family dramas, chit chat fun things.'

I nodded attentively. Yes, I thought to myself, that explains the cow and kettle boiling sounds, the barn door creaking, along with the umm-ing and ah-ing of the aged voices. Just as some people eat so-called comfort food—like rice pudding—this must be comfort radio, a rice-pudding of narrative.

Later on, I returned my flat and commenced a brief online study of *the Archers*. An informed immigrant is a good immigrant. Then I found out that the programme was not only the longest running radio soap in Britain, but the longest in the world. It started in 1950. Originally it aimed to educate farmers and thus increase food production after World War II. But rapidly it became a major source of entertainment for urban as well as rural audiences. Just as we Chinese have 'Peasant Education Channel' public service at home, I guessed? That was how we learned to weave bamboo baskets or cure a sick pig. So should I listen to it too, just to enhance my English as well as my new life in the UK? Perhaps I should not worry about learning the Queen's perfect English, and should start from here, the not so high-brow English in *the Archers*?

Over the next few days, after having submitted myself to

the programme several times during my noodle lunches, I lost any appetite I might have had to join the great listening family of *The Archers*. To describe the programme as a living-death might be a slight exaggeration. After three or four listenings, the theme music induced a strange torpor in my body – an interesting sort of claustrophobia. Then there were the conversations about the minutiae of children's marriages and health. Their conversations seemed to be too indirect, touching on topics like climate change or organic farming, but never ever truly entering. To the din of sirens piercing through my walls, I grew restless. There were no immigrant characters in the story, no serious social debate, no racial problems, no economical crises, no *real* politics. It was an oasis of rural England outside the currents of history. That was its purpose. What else should I have expected? But it was still strange for me. In China we have similar soaps too, the popular ones were always to do with grand love and revolution, but not about domestic ladies living inside a little house and chatting about weather. Only some months later, I learned that the most popular newspapers in Britain were *The Daily Mail* and *The Sun*. Were the readers of these tabloids and the followers of *the Archers* one and the same, I wondered?

Then my thoughts crystalized into a clearer idea. This was an idea about ideology. The most powerful kinds of ideology work by concealment. The apolitical world of *the Archers* was the surface that instilled in its listeners a supremely political position. This was the position of acceptance of the status quo. The Archer's farm was the British state, the animal hierarchy, from chickens up to horses, the mildly entrepreneurial farmers and the middle classes, ever aspirational, fearful of the lower orders, they trudged through the mud and dreamt of the harvest and the sunny uplands. People often don't think the English have ideology. They may think the Chinese are infused by ideology – our revolutionary peasant visions and the Communist system. But not the British! How bizarre. It just goes to show how powerful the ideology in this land is and how effectively people's lives have been shaped and subjugated by it.

I thought this invisibility of ideology was part of the reason why the British, but the English in particular, had this knack for deflecting all direct engagements. Beneath their social surfaces were deeper surfaces, through which they deflected their own thoughts about themselves. They sought insulation from any idea of change. This explained a number of things about the country: people's ability to withstand awful public transport and privatisation of nearly all public utilities and a constant ability to vote against their own interests. Yet there was rebellion, though of a superficial kind. Angry working class teenagers would periodically riot against society in general and loot high street stores. From the 1970s onward there was 'revolution' in the world of pop, which amounted to punk musicians being bad mannered on stage. This was perhaps the existential cry, raw and inebriated, of a jagged reaction to the kettle-boiling and cake-baking families who dwelt eternally in the village of Ambridge, the home of the Archers, the spirit of the English that would never die.

Don't get me wrong. I am not suggesting that the English are anymore ideologically infused than other nations. My essential thought was this. In finding out how ideology works in a country, you find out about a significant aspect of 'national character' in that land.

2.

My next lesson in ideology came several years later. I was sitting in a 'Life in the UK' exam, during an afternoon somewhere in north London. We were in a dim and shabby looking multi-functional community space with two examining officers monitoring us. Next door, a Turkish kebab shop blasted out aloud cacophony from a televised football match. Before I had entered the exam room, I had been waiting in this restaurant, eating a very burnt lamb skewer with a plate of salad. Now the meat was giving me a stomach ache, or was it just the anxiety I was feeling about the exam? Would I fail? I probably would. People say it takes three generation of immigrants to become native, or feel native. In this case, I had to hope that my grandchildren would feel less alien here, assuming they would be willing to stay in this country when they grew up. Maybe they too would be wanderers.

Three weeks before this 'Life in the UK' examination, I had been trying to memorise historical facts about Britain – its monarchical system, The Commonwealth and its countries, as well as legal and social aspects of the UK. Since I was not from a former British colony, I was not familiar with the Parliamentary and Constitutional Monarchy system. Although there was a lot to learn, my efforts to concentrate were not always effective. Moreover, I thought I did not really have to learn things by rote because I thought I had exam technique. Back in China as a school kid, I prided myself on the idea that I had learnt to make the *right* answer for any question. And in most cases there was only one answer anyway. When, however, I found myself in the exam room, I realized, staring at the paper, that was a multiple choice exam:

Please tick the right answer: King Henry VIII's daughter Mary was a devout Catholic who persecuted Protestants, which is why she became known as:

A: Catholic Mary   **B: Contentious Mary**
C: Bloody Mary   **D: Killer Mary**

I cursed myself. What an ignorant immigrant! I should have learnt the difference between Catholic and Protestant, as well as the nicknames of Henry VIII's heir. During my preparation for this test, I was aware that being someone who grew up in a Chinese communist household was a defect for this exam, and I had studied facts such as that women had gained the vote in 1928 in Britain, and that abortion became legal in 1967, and so on and so forth. But I hadn't paid attention to the royal family's nicknames! I regret that I spent most of my days reading 20th century French novels and German politics in my London flat. Now I realized that 20th century European history was not important at all for this exam.

Sitting before my question paper, I randomly ticked the answer B or C, though sometimes with a faint intuition about which was correct. Perhaps an A for a change? As I circled 'Catholic Mary' with my pen, I suddenly had the feeling that I was at risk of losing my British Citizenship. Well, I didn't have British Citizenship yet. I was risking not gaining the qualification I needed for application of my Naturalisation.

As the sub-continental-looking examination officer paced up and down, I thought: why were there no questions about the East India Company or Partition? I exhaled with a long and unsure breath, and moved onto the next question:

Xiaolu Guo

What kind of bird do people usually eat on Christmas Day?

A: Duck   B: Chicken   C: Turkey   D: Ostrich

An easy question at last! Even though previously I only had one Christmas lunch experience in London with an Italian family eating a huge ostrich. Yes, a stuffed ostrich with heavy gravy all over its rubbery flesh. But, on second thoughts, maybe I should not take this question to be as simple as it had seemed to be. When it asked 'people', did it mean 'any people' or 'English people'? As an oriental living in Britain, I always ate a bowl of noodle alone in a rented flat during the Christmas. Santa Claus never visited my chimney, neither friends nor families. Come back to the question: 'What kind of bird...', I disliked eating any kind of bird. I dread the idea of alien hormones from caged chicken farms infesting my stomach. And what about the vegetarians in this country? Was the Christmas spirit incompatible with the consumption of tofu or any sort of bean curd? Or stir fried bok choy in ginger sauce?

Now as I refocused on the exam sheets, letting the flood of dead bird-imagery fade, I quickly ticked the 'C: Turkey' and move on to the next. The next question would be a more serious one, I presumed.

The House of Lords is normally more ___ in the government than the House of Commons.

A: powerful   B: successful
C: independent

Hmm, House of Commons. House of Lords. I always found these expressions odd. It made me think of the Ming

14

Dynasty's East Court and West Court, whose role was to serve the Emperor. That was 500 years ago. For all these years living in London, I had never passed a building with either of these names, *Lords* or *Commons*, on it. Perhaps I had only lived in the poor part of the town? I had a ludicrous image of miniature houses stuck inside the Palace of Westminster and the Queen watering her tulips next to them. Gazing back at the sheets in front of me, I murmured again: *The House of Lords is normally more powerful, or successful, or independent in the government than the House of Commons.* I rescanned the three adjectives. The more I stared at the word 'Lords' and 'Commons', the heavier my eyelids weighed upon me. I needed coffee. Then I thought harder. *Independent* felt like a more neutral word than the pompous vocabulary of *powerful* or *successful*. It suggested democracy, which was the image that the UK liked to project. I marked C. The clock was ticking and I faced the last question with no time to spare.

Which of the following is a country of the UK?

A: Channel Islands   **B: Scotland**
C: Republic of Ireland   **D: Isle of Man**

A country in the UK? What a provocative question for someone from People's Republic of China. I knew Scotland was a country, though without a border with England or using a different passport. I did study aspects of British constitution, and repeatedly read about Britain comprising a number of countries. But still, for me, I could never get used to this idea that this archipelago in the Atlantic should comprise so many different countries rather than provinces. I still remembered reading George Orwell about Englishness: 'We call our islands by no fewer than six different names, England, Britain, Great Britain, the British Isles, the United Kingdom and, in very exalted moments, Albion'. While in my experience, London really seemed to be a different country than the rest of the UK. I sighed, and ticked B.

As I exited the exam room, I had little hope that I would pass. Deep down I think my lack of preparation was not just laziness, or merely the product of preoccupation with other things, but also resistance. There was something about the implicit pride in a supposed thousand years of monarchy, and the parliamentary system – which few I suspected understood – that made me feel ill at ease. It was the same syndrome as *the Archers*. I was just being introduced to the cultural symbols and motifs of the United Kingdom. People learn the history of kings and queens just like we learn fairy tales or consume the latest soap operas. And what for? It's all about instilling the collective wisdom of the ruling classes, yet done in the most bland and innocuous way.

3.

A month later, I received the test result which told me I had passed the exam. So I began to proceed with my naturalisation. Four weeks later, I received a formal letter from the Home Office, congratulating me that I was in the final stage of this long process and I needed to participate in a naturalisation ceremony.

On the day of the ceremony, I put on a newly washed but plain looking coat. My immigrant's experiences made me think in this way: to be normal and to look normal are probably the most appropriate gesture in these circumstances. The last thing you want is to stick out from the crowd. It's not like attending Glastonbury music festival. So I got off the bus near Bow in East London, I stepped into a town hall building, and met with some non-native looking families. They were all well dressed – women in colourful outfit and men in suits. I presumed they were Bengalis or Indians, and a few members of African family. Then there were several white Europeans. The Europeans sat alone with their Iphones in hands, away from us, without any family companions.

In front of a massive portrait of the current Queen, I was given two different coloured sheets. Each one was a printed version of the oath I could read aloud with others. But I had to choose which text I would follow.

The red coloured oath went like this:

fI, [name], swear by Almighty God that, on becoming a British citizen, I will be faithful and bear true allegiance to Her Majesty Queen Elizabeth the Second, Her Heirs and Successors according to law.'

Then the green coloured oath read like this:

'I, [name], will give my loyalty to the United Kingdom and respect its rights and freedoms. I will uphold its democratic values. I will observe its laws faithfully and fulfil my duties and obligations as a British citizen.'

I now knew which oath I would read, and felt relieved that I don't have to read something totally against my beliefs. As if this is not enough, immediately, we were also given a blue piece of paper, on which was written:

Under the Oaths Act 1978, any person who objects to swearing an oath may instead make a solemn affirmation. This also applies when it is not practicable to administer the oath in accordance with a person's religious belief (e.g. if the sacred book of the

*person's religion is not available). The relevant provisions of the
Oaths Act (sections 5 and 6) are applied to citizenship oaths by
section 42 (7) of the British Nationality Act 1981.*

I was totally lost with the gabbled legalese of the blue
paper. Then I found a white sheet underneath it. It read:

*An oral affirmation should be made as follows:
I, [full name], do solemnly, sincerely and truly declare and
affirm that on becoming a British Citizen, I will be faithful
and bear true allegiance to Her Majesty Queen Elizabeth the
Second, Her Heirs and Successors, according to law.*

Words on the paper became a rap song, looping in my ears.
And I began to shake my head left and right with rhythm.
But the Queen's stern looking poster caught my eyes. I could
have sworn for a moment that her eyes were following me.
I recomposed myself and began to look around. Everyone
seemed to be a little lost, especially an elderly lady in her
multi-layered golden sari. Disoriented, I decided to join my
European neighbours and stood beside them. I would just
read any coloured paper that they would be reading. I could
see that they were all holding green paper.

Under the instructions of a respectable looking gentleman
before the Queen, the gathered mass of new citizens read
aloud their oaths in a muffled voice. Male and female, young
and old, Asian and Africans, Europeans and Latinos, we all
trundled along with various level of ease or uneasiness.

*I will give my loyalty to the United Kingdom and respect its
rights and freedoms. I will uphold its democratic values...*

When I was reading those lines, I was almost touched,
especially with the phrase about upholding the democratic

values even though I didn't have any clear vision where Britain would be heading to in the future. Anything could happen. In fact, anything did happen, with the strange escapade of Brexit that later gripped the neck of the country. Though that was the future. But right at this moment we had to do what we were told, in this town hall, in front of the grand looking Elizabeth II held up by plastic poles against the rain drenched window. Just as the characters in *the Archers* must submit themselves to the boggy heaths, water-logged fields submerged in manure, and the still extant medieval system of land ownership, we, citizens of the UK must live in our eternal village of Ambridge – assuming the borders are still safely guarded. I could feel the weight of my submission bearing down on me. I would mouth the empty words ordained by the state, and I would bend, genuflect and submit to the dull mantras that trickled down from the heights of power.

As my thoughts were propelled upwards through the tuneless humming of the collective mass, the national anthem resonated in my ears and took on the guise of an epiphany. Had I seen the light? I feared there was no light to be seen. I sang, zombie-like:

God save all dressed in green
Long live our noble Queen
God save the Queen
Send her victorious
Happy and glorious
Long to reign over us

Getting Better
Viola Di Grado

Translated by Antony Shugaar

It started with a knocking.

I say a knocking because a regular rapping sound at the door is always a signal for us: there's someone looking for you, someone who wants to come into your world, bringing affection or threats.

But it wasn't really a knocking.

It was a heavy noise, smothered somehow, like a head being smashed hard against the door.

At four in the morning, in my small, shadowy apartment on Camden Road, someone was banging their head against the door.

That was my third night living there.

It was an ex-council house, one of those houses built in Victorian England for the penniless and the homeless, then sold off by the government to private citizens for a song.

Buildings with excessively fragile and precarious structures, unsuitable for life, disguised years later as real houses.

The first time I'd seen the apartment—a month before, in September, just after getting off the train with my sister—the place was full of construction workers in tweed shirts and tools.

The panes of the only window, in the bedroom with its rhomboid floor plan, were fogged and streaked, pocked and eroded by sleet and wind. As soon as I set foot in the room some impulse had driven me to draw the blinds.

'What are you doing?' my sister asked me.

'Nothing… the light.'

'What about the light?'

I needed a place to live right away, and this place was dirt cheap.

After I was done with detox, I needed a new space, not impregnated with my memories, like the clinic was.

Nobody liked the clinic but me.

I also liked the public hospital in Bloomsbury where I'd wound up a month before, forearms swollen and bluish, after passing out in the frozen food aisle at Tesco. I liked these places because they had no identities, they were places with starched white sheets and walls unadorned by pictures.

Each of these places was another limbo where you could purge yourself of the evil in your body, the poison and the yearning for more poison. I still longed for heroin, but only in my head now: my body had unlearned that desire.

That's why I was no longer in the clinic, being closely observed and monitored and kept under lock and key like a repugnant little girl, but instead in an ordinary dimension where I was expected to look after my own survival and the world paid me no mind.

*

I'd signed, my sister wanted me to sign, you could tell from her tense gaze and the darting movements of her pupils, she wanted to be rid of that worry.

Rid of me.

I was the worst thought on her mind.

I'd signed, then the pen had fallen out of my hand and rolled across the floor five feet, until it vanished under the sofa.

One of the construction workers, a very tall man with eyes the color of ice, had picked it up, saying as he did so: 'The floors aren't level, that's one thing we can't do a thing about.'

I'd gone into the bathroom, a little shaken up, my hair clammy with sweat.

'In a month, it'll all be different,' said a voice from behind the door.

It was my sister, I thought, referring hopefully to my future, but instead it was the landlady, and she was talking about the renovations.

Actually, the problem hadn't been drugs.

At least, not strictly speaking.

For me, heroin was just a passing glitch, something that had happened to me while I was trying to blunt the edge of my sadness with every chemical method known to mankind.

Something that had taken up too much room in my body and then in my mind, like what happens in the most ordinary kind of relationship, and in fact all that it really would have taken—as I knew—was a little perseverance and self-respect to put an end to it then and there.

The real problem was the affection.

The affection with which family members and coworkers,

friends, and friends of friends, were suddenly inundating me.

I felt humiliated by their affection.

A clingy, sticky, regressive affection, made up of pity and condescension and spangled with overly solicitous kindness. An affection spawned and grafted, historically, from decades of indie films about drug addicts, broadcast on TV.

An affection stirred by a sensation of death; everyone can sense death in a junkie and this is the way they react: on the inside, they're laughing with joy because *they're* not the ones whose lives are in danger, on the outside they're giving you hugs because you actually are, *you're* the one whose obituary they'll read some Sunday morning in Regent's Park, between an ice cream cone and a stroll around the lake, or who they'll hear mentioned in a lazy late-night conversation at the tail end of a party, when everyone has long-since run out of gossip to regale the other guests with, and when someone drunker or simply meaner than the others will mention your name, eyes gleaming like a wild beast, and they'll say, do you remember *her*, do you know how she died, poor thing? You're the one they may find someday by the side of the road, on the curb, lying in the dogshit, overdosing—you're the one who'll make them all feel just how safe they are.

The day I moved in, it really was all different.

The windows shut hermetically; the panes of glass were intact. The corpses of moths had disappeared from the nooks and crannies, and so had the little spiders from behind the radiators.

The cracks in the ceilings and the mold in the corners and the flaking on the walls had all vanished. The rooms had been filled with shiny new furniture, breakable but efficient. The floors had been taken up and replaced with fake shiny hardwood parquet, which still preserved that off-kilter angle.

It was good enough for normal living, and that's all anyone asks of a house, a normal life.

The house had been cleaned and gone over inch by inch and rebuilt, but it was still a ghost of a house, vulnerable, run through from one end to the other by sounds and chills.

Through the walls came the sound of the rain and the mingled whisperings of all the neighbours.

When I walked through the rooms, I could feel a void under my feet, like the cushion of air when an airplane is coming in for a landing. When I dropped my lipstick or a drinking glass onto the floor, it would hurry quickly over to the far side of the room.

In the morning, when I left my bedroom and went to the kitchen, I felt nauseous and my head ached. At night, the drawers in the bedside table would suddenly fly open, and fall to the floor with a tremendous crash.

The next morning I went to Camden Market.

There was a light drizzle and almost no one out and about on the streets.

The sky was still and grey, like the ceiling of an office building.

I bought a set of antique photographs of London.

I went home and plastered the walls with those pictures.

My sister would be coming over for lunch the next day and I couldn't wait for her to see how pretty I'd made the house.

That's the only way she'd understand.

That everything was different, that I was different.

On the living room walls, I posted a blurry photograph of Tavistock Square, from the time when Virginia Woolf still lived there, and not the anonymous hotel that it was now.

And then Camden Lock, before it was a market for tourists, but was still just a labyrinth of dark, stony alleys, full of punkers who thought they could change the world, and not people with mohawks fresh from the hairdresser, offering to take a picture with you for a pound.

And then a pink-stone building on the Regent's Canal, which was later demolished. Then views of Oxford Street before it became an unbroken expanse of chain stores and shopping malls. When I was done hanging up those pictures, I realized that they were all photographs of places that had later been destroyed or corrupted, ruined once and for all.

The next day I cooked rice with salmon and then made a salad with beets and peas. Last of all, I baked a red velvet cake, her favorite. I had to bake two cakes, because the first one didn't come out quite right.

Then I put on my best clothes.

The sweater that she had given me four years ago, red and black with a turtleneck, then a pair of corduroy trousers that I'd ironed for the occasion. I put on makeup, foundation and red lipstick, a light application of eyeliner.

My heart was pounding.

I sat down on the sofa, back straight, wafting perfume in all directions, waiting for the doorbell to ring.

By two thirty, she still hadn't arrived.

Forlorn, I went outside to make sure that the intercom worked.

I pushed the doorbell: the chilly, austere racket rang through the empty apartment.

*

I went in and grabbed my phone.

I dialed my sister's number.

She didn't answer.

A minute later I got a message from her on WhatsApp.

Sorry I can't come. Maybe next time: Kisses.

I threw the food into the trash can.

Sure, I could have eaten it, but now it felt as if it had been contaminated by all the emptiness I was feeling.

I flopped down onto the sofa, turned on the TV, then turned it off and looked at the blank screen until I dropped off to sleep.

The following week, at work, I kept myself busy with the more complicated projects, to keep from thinking. I was a graphic designer for an ad agency, I wracked my brains over images that meant nothing, then I'd say in meetings: there's no soul, there, in this, there's not enough happiness.

Every now and then my sister would send me smiley faces and emojis of various kinds, but only in response to messages I'd send her.

In response to me telling her we need to see each other.

In response to the picture I sent her of the window in my office when dried leaves flew against the glass.

In response to the picture of the chicken-and-avocado sandwich I bought at Russell Square on my lunch break.

In response to me writing to her *have you seen what a beautiful sunny day it is? London looks like it's been covered with gold dust!! Why don't you ever come see me? The apartment is full of new things, I even have that gadget you make crêpes with, if you come over I'll make you a delicious crêpe with truffles and then we can sit on the sofa together and watch a movie like when we were kids.*

*

My sister never never came over.

Autumn ended and the winter began.

The sky was always gray or milky white.

One game I played was to drop my earrings and pendants and gold chains and lipstick caps on the floor and watch them roll away from one end of the room to the other, fetching up under the furniture, under the sofa: I imagine I was in flight and all my things fell off me and tumbled down, in free fall, until they disappeared from sight.

That night, November 28th, the knocking just kept getting louder and louder.

I got up.

I opened the door.

On the doormat, curled up, his knees pulled tight to his chest, was a naked, elderly man.

Bony, fair-skinned, belly taut and protruding. The exhausted face of an old man, scalp lacerated beneath the line of his sparse white hair.

He gazed at me, with a searching, imploring gaze, like an animal waiting for its daily ration of food.

Only then did I notice the wings.

Limp and iridescent, dark brown, they sprouted from his back and lay softly folded on the floor.

I went inside and locked the door behind me.

I went back out almost immediately.

'Who are you?'

He didn't answer.

He looked up at me, his breathing labored.

'Are you able to stand up?'

He didn't answer.

Maybe he didn't understand my language.

I dragged him inside.

He was as light as a bag of packing peanuts.

Though his hands looked withered and gnarled, they were soft and slick as rubber.

I eased him onto the sofa.

My sofa was beat up and old, purchased used from a charity shop on Camden High Street. The creature went on looking at me with that same sad look on his face, sitting with his back straight, as if judging me. It was intolerable.

'I let you in. I've been good. You shouldn't look at me like that.'

No answer.

My nerves shot, I went into the bathroom, slamming the door behind me. I looked at myself in the mirror, the premature wrinkles, the deep dark circles under my eyes.

'I've been good. You shouldn't look at me like that.'

I felt an old impulse, the one that had once led my brain to give a command to my hands, whereupon a drawer would slide open, and out would come the syringes.

But now that impulse was untranslatable, it was an abstract thing, like a piece of bad poetry.

I emptied the drawer anyway, and instead of syringes I found candle ends and rusted razors, dried-out tubes of toothpaste, a jar of hand cream, a postcard of an angel in flight.

Why hadn't the previous tenants emptied the drawers?

I turned the postcard over.

The angel was clumsily painted.

On the back, in the lines deployed to host Christmas greetings, there was nothing written.

I imagined my mother had sent it to me from the afterlife, but that was just some sad and meaningless thought, and it was sad and meaningless thoughts in the first place that had made me a repugnant junkie, so I pushed the drawer shut again.

When I came out of the bathroom, the creature was no longer there.

I lay down on the bed with the postcard.

An hour later I woke back up with a start.

I felt a hot breath on my neck.

I switched on the bedside lamp in a fit of terror.

It was him again.

Wrapped tight around my body like a monkey.

Looking at him now from so close, it was obvious that he was an angel.

He was ugly, misshapen, and old for an angel, but still that's what he was.

His hair was wispy and sparse and white, his face was pale and covered with blemishes, dark pockmarks and scattered bristly hairs, black and whitish, gray, straw blonde. There were hairs in his nostrils, too.

'Tell me something. Tell me why you're here.'

No answer.

'Are you here for me?'

Silence.

'Are you here for me or by chance?'

Silence.

I turned off the light and went to sleep.

*

The next day I gave him a bath.

I scrubbed at his skinny shoulders with the shower sponge, the bruises on his back where the wings sprouted. I delicately brushed his wings with a wide-toothed comb. They were sparse, opaque, like the feathers of bird carcasses I'd found on Primrose Hill, once, when I was a girl.

He had no genitalia. I kept asking him questions, but then it became clear to me that he didn't know how to talk, or maybe he just didn't find talking to be useful. I didn't leave the house because I was afraid he'd break a windowpane and try to fly away.

'It wouldn't work,' I kept telling him, shower sponge in hand, but his gaze was fixed and registered nothing.

For lunch, I cooked him an array of different things because I didn't know what he liked to eat. Spinach, broccoli, grilled cheese, pasta with tuna, panna cotta. He looked at each of the dishes with no expression whatsoever, then went back to gazing into the distance.

I gave up and lay down on the sofa in exhaustion.

The angel sat down next to me, took my arm, and started slowly licking it.

I was surprised, disgusted, and yet at the same time overwhelmed by a mysterious wave of tenderness.

I sat, motionless, and I let him do it.

His tongue was rough and dripping with saliva, like a dog's tongue.

His tongue lingered on all the holes in my arm. The holes where needles had plunged in like teeth to flood me with junk. Every time that it lingered on a hole, I felt a pleasurable shock.

Viola Di Grado

When he was done, my eyes were streaming with tears, and I looked down at my arm: the holes, the sinister marks of my pathetic Calvary, had vanished.

I phoned my sister.

'Now what is it?'

Her voice was weary, annoyed.

I was tempted to hang up.

'I'm all better now.'

'You've said it so many times, I'm sick of hearing you say it, do you hear me? I'm sick of keeping after you and watching you trip and fall every time.'

'No. No. This time it's different. You have to come see.'

'See what?'

'Umm... I wouldn't know how to explain it. I can't.'

'If this is just some way of getting me to come over to your house, if this is just...'

'No, I swear it isn't.'

'I can't take care of you anymore, do you get that? You're going to have to make it on your own.'

My hand was shaking.

'I'm all better, I swear I am.'

'I have to go.'

I turned to look at the angel.

He was in the same position as before.

I sat down again beside his elderly body, I looked at the varicose veins on his bony thighs and the deep creases on his long hands. The chipped, purplish fingernails. The dark circles beneath his glassy, staring eyes.

I started kissing him.

I tasted the bitter flavor of his breath, his chipped teeth. I was disgusted but full of an impetus unlike anything I'd ever felt before, like the empty air beneath a plane during takeoff.

He sat motionless.

Then, all at once, his wings spread open. They were gigantic, like a silvery tent.

They opened and then closed over us, over his body and mine, curled up next to his.

The next morning I woke up filled with joy.

I opened my eyes.

He wasn't there.

I looked for him everywhere in the house, my heart in my mouth the whole time.

At the center of the room, piled up, were all my earrings and rings, fine silver chains, all the things I had let slip away onto the floor until it vanished behind the furniture.

I went outside.

I was shouting out sounds, senseless and nameless.

I went down Camden Road in the snow, until Camden Lock, where the horse hospital had once stood. I searched for him in the midst of the crowd, among the Chinese offering fried chicken run through with skewers, the Slavic women extending their arm to let you feel a fast waxing on your forearm. Anxiety filled my chest, cutting off my breath, I had to stop in the crowd and struggle for air. My head filled with senseless images, bird carcasses on Primrose Hill, burst open with some secret malady, intestines spouting from amongst the plumage.

And then his face.

His face.

I realized I already couldn't remember his face anymore.

All this is real, it must be real: London in the winter, the neglected grass on the open space, the white houses along the road that runs up from Chalk Farm, the bridge covered with graffiti, the homeless women reaching her hand out toward me. All this is real, the angel and my unmarked arms. I hurried into a cafeteria restroom, I pulled back my sleeves to check, then I felt a sudden pressure on my back.

Something growing, frail but hopeful.

Like grass beneath the snow, like flower bulbs buried in the bones.

I walked out of the cafeteria, the sun was shining, and with a smile on my face I turned toward home and started walking.

The Film Shop
Saleh Addonia

I

Two lovers, a prince and a princess sit on a carpet. The carpet
floats on a small lake. A tree sliced in half. A village. A donkey
drags a cart. Pots. Those were some of the images that stayed
with me from a Japanese film that I once saw late at night either
on BBC2 or Channel4. I was stoned. In those days, I didn't have
a VHS player, so I used to get stoned and wait till after 12 am
for foreign films to be shown on television because they were
subtitled. Years later, when I was perusing the shelves of The
Film Shop on Liverpool Road, I instantly recognised the cover
image: Mizoguchi's Ugetsu Monogatari or Tales of Moonlight
and Rain. But the two lovers weren't a prince and a princess
but a poor villager and a ghost. They weren't floating but
reclining in ecstasy on a large picnic blanket laid over a patch
of grass. The tree wasn't sliced but two trees, standing next to
each other. The cart wasn't dragged by a donkey but by a man
with his brother pushing it at the back.

I was sad when Gabrielle told me that The Film Shop, would close down. At that time, I was hardly renting any films as I was busy writing a film script. The film shop used to open at 4 pm and normally got busy after 5 pm, so I had an hour or so to talk to Gabrielle; she behind the desk and I in front of her. Gabrielle used to read my film scripts, and I hers. We'd spend the hour exchanging ideas and opinions. Gabrielle was a filmmaker and was born in the hometown of Jane Eyre's author. Though I rented and watched a film adaptation of the book, I couldn't fail but notice the surprise in Gabrielle's eyes when I told her that I never read the Brontë sisters.

I asked myself why I hadn't joined a long time ago. I'd often passed by. But it wasn't until I was told I'd be made redundant from my job as a photographic technician that I went inside. I walked aimlessly through the streets of Islington the day after that news, and stopped by the window of The Film Shop. For a £10 monthly fee I could rent up to 3 films a day. Why not? I'd have time. I glanced at the Barnsbury job centre on my way home thinking that I'd be back there in a month's time. Each day for the next four weeks, I worked at Photofusion in Brixton, then late in the evenings when most of the staff had left, printed hundreds of pages of articles about world cinema directors to take home and read.

Almost every day unemployed I sat in a café in Goswell Street. The cafe owner would change the name of the cafe from time to time; sometimes, it was café @ or Fuck Coffee or Fuck me Coffee or Goswell Road Coffee. Whatever its name was, I was there on the mornings from around seven-ish (sometimes in the winter from around six-thirty-ish so I could experience the darkness morphing into light) and in the afternoons from around four-ish. Though in the winter, I'd go as early as three because of the early sunset. I sat at a favourite spot opposite a large window and did nothing for an hour or two. I talked to no one and no one talked to me. My brain recalled films I'd seen or dreamed up films I wanted to make. My eyes observed the passers-by. And sometimes, my brain, eyes and heart would collaborate and concentrate on a whole duration: I'd look without any interruption from the moment when someone or something enters the window frame until he, she or it leaves it. Be it any living being or even a leaf at the mercy of the winds. I once saw a child tie a red balloon to a street litter bin and leave the frame. The balloon was dancing on the air. I watched the balloon for more than half hour and I was expecting it to fly away at any moment until she entered the frame and punctured the balloon with her cigarette butt. I saw her, I believe, more than eleven whole durations on days after that. In each duration, I had different emotion. She would enter from the left side of the window, with her bobbed haircut, and always smoking. The second time I saw her, was from her back for almost the whole duration. And there was this duration where she was talking on her mobile phone and smoking while looking directly at me or at her nails, that may have been freshly airsprayed at the Chinese nail salon nearby. Then she disappeared for a while. But I saw her coming out of a phone box, holding call cards. I felt as if I saw someone famous. The lady in so many silent frames. I almost waved my hands at her, and wanted to shout, 'Hi!' But before I could do that, she stood facing me. She looked at me coldly. She then gave me one of the call cards and walked away. I looked at the picture on the card, it wasn't her, and there was a name on the card: Nananana. I really wanted to ask her if they'd give any discounts for someone as unemployed like me. But she instantly disappeared from my view. I saw her for the final time, when she entered the frame, wearing a black boucle coat. And then as she was trying to cross the street, she was run over by a pizza delivery boy on a motorbike. I don't know if she lived or died but I didn't leave my seat.

Gabrielle complained about spiralling rent costs, Pirate Bay and Bit Torrent, LoveFilm, Netflix and Apple releasing its macs without DVD players. However, she also told me that the owner – who once recommended me The Third Part of the Night, a Polish film that I too would recommend to anyone, but I wouldn't want to see again – was willing to sell if he could find a buyer.

When it comes to sound, I am man+machine. And this fusion with the machine reproduces, badly, the sounds from TV, Radio or phone. And it is even worse with an immediate human natural speech, where, nor me, my doctor, my audiologist or friends will know when or what I will hear, if it isn't a one to one situation in a quiet room. That is why - when I am watching films - I rely entirely on subtitles, including for English language films. So, I see and read films at the same time (I normally have to sacrifice one or the other). The average speed of human speech is around 180 words per mins, but with Orson Welles's films, I suspect, the average speed exceeds double that. People talking fast all the time, and a voice-over decorates every frame, and the camera pans and moves too. And I have to watch his images for 2 hours at 360 words a minute. Painful!

Gabrielle told me that a film producer, an Islingtonian, was willing to buy The Film Shop provided he gets a concrete idea for revamping the shop. I told Gabrielle about what Godard said of American cinema (almost all of Godard's one liners have now became a cliché): that Hollywood only makes one film a year. So, I asked her to tell the owner about my idea to replace the American section (aside from the classics) and triple their collection of world cinema, find and add out of print DVDs. The next day, Gabrielle told me the would-be owner said 'no.' I then proposed that to reinvent The Film Shop as a Film and Theatre Café. And again, replacing the American section (aside from the classics) with theatre DVDs. There were a few theatres nearby such as Almeida theatre, King's Head Theatre Pub and Old Red Lion Theatre Pub, and perhaps they could attract more customers from those spaces. The would-be owner's answer, through Gabrielle, was negative. As the deadline for its closure loomed, I pleaded with Gabrielle to tell this faceless would-be owner that I was prepared to design a leaflet appeal to save the shop (I had already designed a DVD cover for one of Gabrielle's award winning short films), and that I would distribute this leaflet myself to every house in Islington. I knew I could do this because I once worked as Pizza leaflet ad distributor. I knew every single street in Islington. The operation would be easy for me, and all of this free of charge. But again, the answer was negative.

Every day, I used to take different routes to go to The Film Shop and different ones to get back to my flat in Kings Cross. The only streets I avoided were the streets that lead to the Jobcentre. Sometimes I wondered if I was hallucinating. There was such contrast between my silent room and the roar in the nearby streets. My moods would swing from low to high. If I saw the Islingtonians in the streets, our eyes would meet but to only for them to veer and look the other way. Or I'd look down at the pavement or through the Islingtonians' windows, at the ground floor or basement; the kitchens or living rooms. And there were those occasions when I'd walk at dawn or an hour before. The streets would be empty, and I'd even notice the lampposts being switched off. On one late morning, I was in a low mood. I stood next to a Flight Centre branch in Upper Street. The foot of my right leg was resting on the wall behind me. I was staring at the sky, waiting for the partial eclipse of the sun. All of a sudden, I saw three Italian women, seemingly in high spirits, walk past me and into an office. I believed my eyes. I guessed that they were Italian because of the way they gesticulated as they spoke. One was blonde and the other two, brunettes. They were dressed in Eritrean traditional dress (white woven cotton clothing) and had their hair braided in traditional Eritrean style (in London, I have seen western women dressed in west African dress, Chinese, Indian or Tibetan dresses but I'd never seen one wearing an Eritrean dress). But then the blonde one, who had a sad look in her eyes when she stopped conversing with her friends, stood outside the door and looked up at the sky and then at the door or perhaps at me. I thought I saw her lips moving, and I said, 'Are you talking to me?' I watched her moving past me as if I were a statue and through the open door.

The Film Shop closed down when I was set to embark on a study of silent cinema. The idea of the study came to me, when suddenly, the battery of my hearing aid ran out while I was in the cafe. I kept my hearing aid on but heard only muffled sound from the outside world and the constant low buzzes and hums from inside. It was Sunday afternoon. There was a DJ playing Drum and Bass music, which turned to nothing but a low thud. I was sitting on a two-seat sofa. An old man sat at the sofa opposite me. He was holding a glass of white wine, his hand shaking. He put the glass down to close to the edge of the table. I looked at it for a few seconds, but I couldn't warn him because I don't like to speak when I cannot hear my own voice. The glass fell to the floor. The old man didn't move at all. An elderly waitress came. She picked up 5 large fragments of the broken glass, with her hands, one at a time and put them on the dust pan. Holding a sponge with her left hand, she wiped the floor a few times. I tried to count the number of the wipes she did without success. Using the sponge, the waitress picked up the remaining small fragments of the glass and put them onto the dustpan. She got up and walked away.

One afternoon, I was at the café reading a DVD supplement of Humanity and Paper Balloons. In the supplement, it said that its director Sadao Yamanaka - a close friend of Tokyo Story director Ozo – was visited by Kurosawa when he was still an assistant director during the shoot of the film. The Seven Samurai director remembered that even though the weather was perfectly fine, everybody was just standing around idly, peering up at the sky. He learnt they were waiting for a cloud to waft over a warehouse on the set... Just then I saw a woman with a Great Dane sitting opposite me on the sofa. Garbo, I wanted to shout. She really looked like Greta Garbo. I had a cut-out picture of Garbo, looking down, with her index finger on her forehead after I read, somewhere, that she was the idea of beauty in Cinema. But my Garbo picture was in Black & White and this woman's eyes were green with thick red painted lips. Could she be related to Garbo? Perhaps she was her great granddaughter. But Garbo never married or had any children, so perhaps, a great granddaughter of a cousin. The woman, looked at the DVD cover on the table, and said, 'You like At..aus movs?' I lipread.

'What?' I said, giving into uncomfortable speech.

The woman looked at me and then at my hearing aid, and said loudly, 'DO YOUUU LIKE AAAART HAAAAOOOS MOVIIIIES?'

'Yes,' I said.

'AMAAAZING... AMAZING!' the woman shouted again and kept nodding her head while looking at me. And then, she shouted, 'HAAVE YOU WAAATCHED ALII FEEEAR EEEEATS THA SOOOUL?'

'No,' I said. Now, I became convinced that she isn't related to Garbo because she has an English accent, and that because she had her dog with her, then she must be a local, an Isilngtonian, perhaps.

'FAAASBINDAAAR. FAAASBINDAAAR,' the woman said.

'Not yet,' I said, 'But I know Fassbinder...'

'It is an AMAZING MOOOVIE. AAALI REMIINDS MEEEE OOOF YOU...' the woman shouted.

'Thank you. I will watch it.'

'YOU ARE AMAZING!'

'I want to be alone. I want to be left alone.'

I signed on every fortnight, on Tuesday mornings. I hated those mornings! It was on those mornings that I sunk low and felt useless. My depression would begin on Monday evenings. And it would go on until I was on my way to the Jobcentre, which was 15 mins walk from where I lived. And during those 15 minutes my worries would intensify wondering whether she, my job coach, would accept the list of job searches that I had conducted, applied for or would apply for. In truth, I hadn't searched or applied for any jobs at all. Instead, I took notes while I watched films. Once inside the Jobcentre, a large open plan office, I had to wait to be called in by my job coach. The time would pass too slowly, even if I had to wait just 5 minutes. In those times, I'd pretend to read a book. And the book would be very close to my face, almost covering it so that I was not seen. So that nobody could make eye contact. Trust me, when you are in a Jobcentre, you don't want to show your parasite-like face to either the staff or the others who have parasite-like faces like you. When I met my job coach in a small private and glass framed space, I'd recount, of course, my job-hunting news. I once told her that I rewrote my CV so that I could apply for a job as a black cab driver. After a brief pause, she said, 'It takes the average person between 2 to 4 years to learn the blue book'. She suggested looking instead for a job as a mini cab driver. But I replied that, due to my deafness, I would not be able to take job details over the radio or by phone. Then I went home knowing that I'd have 13 more days to watch films. Another time I told my job coach that I was looking for a job as a hairdresser. But then and suddenly, my job coach turned her face away from me. I saw her face sadden and tears cloud her eyes.

'I was a hairdresser,' she said, 'I had a salon. I met my late husband Antony there. He was one of my customers.'

She paused, then carried on without looking at me, 'He committed suicide a few days after we got married. Not long after, I sold the salon, left my town and moved to London...'

'I am really sorry...' I said, staring at her beautiful, ageing face.

'Anyway,' she interrupted, 'You wouldn't be able to do this job. It involves a lot of listening to customers. You need to look at their hair rather than their face and you rely mostly on the lips to hear people...'

'What a shame!' I lied, 'I really wanted to meet new people and make friends.'

I walked a lot with Bef, around the streets of Islington. Bef worked in Islington Local History Centre as a Heritage Officer. Once, we walked around Barnsbury and I asked him to tell me something about it.

'The Barnsbury tdy...' Bef said.

'Wait, wait,' I interrupted Bef. I moved to his left side as my hearing aid is on my right ear, 'Go on.'

'Its nEt treets, well mantaned houses... lanscape square, shops... botiik, is...' Bef said

'Say that again,' I said.

'The streets are uncogisabl from the povety years foowing th Second Wod Waar,' Bef said.

'Can you tell me about the residents?' I asked.

'Leaf wing and labour suppotres...'

'Can you say that again,' I interrupted.

'Laber SUPPORTERS,' said Bef, 'They were acchticts, panners...'

'Wait! WAIT,' I interrupted, 'Let the truck pass.'

It was a large goods vehicle. We waited till the truck's noise receded. 'Where were we?' I asked.

'Those new residents fomed the Bansbury Assoshin... and saved old building from demotion...'

'Demoation?'

'Demolition,'Bef shouted, 'I am tired of repeating.'

'Who lives in Bransbury?'

'Middle-class...middle-class. Fashionable middle-class. Metropolitans class.'

'Where are the working class?'

'Shit out...'

'What?'

'SHIPPED out!'

'To where?'

Bef pointed towards Caledonian road, and said 'The tower boocks, in Caddonian road.'

'Were they happy to move out?' I asked

'I said,' Bef shouted, 'SHIPPED OUT!'

'I heard there are new gentry now days.' I said

'They are banks...' Bef said.

'Banks!'

'Bankers, BANKERS!

'What happened to the middle class?'

'Most ass been outpiced...'

'What? Out pissed...spicid?'

'No! OUTPRICED. OUTPRICED! I am tired of shouting,' Bef shouted

Bef was one of the people who rarely complained about repeating words for me. Bef was born in Ethiopia, Addis Ababa. He arrived in London with his parents, aged five. Bef studied at SOAS, University of London, the history and geography of Africa. He joined The Foreign Legion when he couldn't find a job in London. But his career in the Legion

12 222 1222222 222222222

ended in a court martial and he moved to Addington, south of Croydon. When Bef began working in Islington, he was still writing his memoires. I read part of them in which Bef recalls the heat of Djibouti and his beautiful young local girlfriend, Raheela. Bef was a chief of his section when he was discharged. A handsome young man joined the Legion and Bef grew jealous of him and his popularity. He sent the young man on an expedition without a compass and to his death in the harsh deserts of the Afar region, in the borders between Djibouti and Ethiopia.

At The Film Shop, Ritjana chose her favourite film - Pasolini's Medea - and I Tsai Ming Liang's I Don't Want to Sleep Alone. At home, I said to Ritjana, while trying to conceal my smile, 'Since I have seen Medea it would be better to watch,' I pointed at the DVD title, I don't want to sleep alone, 'You've watched Medea...,' Ritjana stared at me and then asked what the film was about. I thought for a while, and said, 'It is about the body and a double mattress. The suppressed emotions, desire and longings. ...and love'

While we were watching I Don't Want to Sleep Alone, I kept on looking at Ritjana through the corners of my eyes. On the one hand, I was hoping that she wouldn't get bored as words are rarely spoken in the film. And on the other, that she may get aroused; there are lots of sexual scenes without them being pornographic. Ritjana's eyes, during the entire film, were fixated on the screen. When the film finished, she exclaimed, 'Wow! Wow! What a film. This is my favourite film now!' Later on, we went to Kings Head Theatre Pub, in Upper Street. But we were thrown out after Ritjana drunkenly flashed her boobs at me while we were sitting on one of the theatre seats. The theatre was at the back of the bar and normally opened its doors for regulars after a play ended. As I was walking Ritjana to Caledonian road, so she could take the bus to go home to her husband, we stopped at Lonsdale Square. We kissed passionately and then I climbed the metal rails of the garden on impulse, hoping we could have a little privacy. But Ritjana couldn't jump; she had a prosthetic leg.

I once asked Gabrielle about the shop's main customers. 'Posh,' she said, loudly. I not only heard her say 'P' but the 'oosh'. I then asked her, 'What are they like?' 'POOSH,' she said, loudly again, shrugging her shoulder. 'What kind of films do they rent?' I asked. She pointed to the Hollywood commercial section on her right.

Job seekers allowance was scarcely enough to pay for my bills and food. I couldn't go out apart from to a café, twice a day, to drink the cheapest coffee or tea. The only time I went out for a drink, was when a friend would invite me and pay for me. Most of the time, I went out with Bef. My financial situation was getting harder by the day. Once I was on a crowded train when I saw a man holding a broadsheet newspaper, folded in half, moving closer to a man in a suit. I watched closely. I saw him edge towards the man in the suit in the crowded carriage till their bellies touched each other. As the train was about to stop, the man with the paper folded the newspaper with his right hand and then with his left. I knew the man's wallet was inside. When the doors of the train opened, the man with the paper quickly left the train carriage. I bought a book titled: The Prince of Pickpockets by Richard S. Lambert. I read it day and night and practiced pickpocketing at home. I used a small notebook and drilled myself in picking it out with my index and middle finger from the inside pocket of my jacket. I also hung my jacket at the back of my room's door, put my wallet on my jacket's pocket and practiced picking it using a newspaper, like the pickpocket on the tube. I took the Victoria line from Oxford street. I stood in front of a man wearing a black suit. I looked at him while pretending to read the newspaper that I held with both hands. I got closer to the man while my heart was pounding. I looked him in the eye. He too, looked me directly in the eye. And he kept on looking at me as I was inching closer. As the train stopped, I got totally freaked out and I abandoned my plans. I got out of the train and sat at one of the benches in Kings Cross station platform, with my heart still pounding. I met Bef most of Friday evenings for a drink or two – he normally paid for them – at my local pub. On one of those Fridays, we were both standing at the bar counter facing each other. Once the bar got busier, I pushed myself into Bef. I slid my right hand, then my index and middle fingers into his inside jacket's pocket. Quickly and smoothly, I picked out his wallet. I dropped it and caught it with my left hand at the hem of his jacket. I went to the toilet. I found £80 in Bef's wallet. I took out a ten and a twenty-pound note and put them in my pocket. I went back to the bar and managed to slip Bef's wallet back inside one his outside pockets. From then on, I kept on pushing myself against Bef and pickpocketing him, every now and then. I was learning new skills and hoping, soon enough, I'd use them in the trains at St Pancras train station.

It isn't my history and I should steer clear of making judgment, but perhaps the English don't like the present. For whatever reasons, they choose to ignore present conditions and concentrate instead on the past. So I thought, when I passed Thornhill Square. The square was full of vans and trucks loaded with filming equipment. The technical crews were getting the lighting and camera tracks ready for, I presume, a scene or two for a period drama. I was seized by a sudden fit of depression when I saw, among all the people and trucks, the director's chair. The director was surrounded by his crew, standing behind him. The director, shouted, 'Camera! Action! Don't move!'

A man, wearing a black suit and a tie was sitting in a white bench, opposite a woman who was looking at him. The woman was wearing a black turtleneck mini dress and a necklace. They were surrounded by garden leaves. The man said, '… That was the day I photographed you, and you asked me to give you a year. Perhaps to test me, perhaps to weary me, or so you could forget. But time is important…'

'Cut!' The assistant director, shouted,

'What the fuck!' the director shouted,

The assistant director leaned in and said loudly, close to the director's right ear and into his hearing aid, 'He forgot his lines! He said, important…'

The director said, 'Oh! Not again. It is unimportant! But time is UNIMPORTANT! …'

After Ritjana dumped me, I tried to avoid watching films about love. But perusing The Film Shop's shelves was painful because I had to read the films' synopsis at the back of the DVD covers. And on many occasions, I ended up reading about love. And so, most of the time I'd come out with films that I had seen before. And sometimes, I'd go home without renting any films, but once I was home, I'd remember 1, 2 or 3 things I knew about her. One early morning, I woke from a bad dream. A really bad dream. In my dream, I tried to engineer my own death by burying myself alive after the contract killer I hired hadn't turn up to shoot me outside The Film Shop at the sunrise. He was one of three contract killers I met. The other two not only refused but questioned me about the morality of suicide, even though I was offering them money to do it.

I carried on dreaming. My mother stood motionless behind my brother and me. Perhaps she was thinking about our absent father, who was fighting with the Eritrean Liberation Front (ELF) in the war of independence against Ethiopia. My brother spilt milk on the sand while we were eating our breakfast on the ground in our hut. Our black cat tried to lap up the milk but only for the sands to absorb it. My brother spilt sugar from the palm of his hand onto the black cat's fur. My mother shouted, 'Fire!' I ran and stopped by the door of our hut. Our neighbour's hut was on a fire and the sky was raining.

*

When I was a member of The Film Shop, I used the phone booth quite a lot after Virgin Media, my landline provider, cut off my landline because I hadn't paid my bills for months. I had a Pay as You Go Mobile phone, but it wasn't compatible with my hearing aid. Sometimes, I used to walk long distances to find a working kiosk. People were using them less and less, and as a result BT lost interest in their maintenance. One day, I saw more than a dozen of pigeons flying around me. I didn't pay much attention to them. But soon they began annoying me. They were literally following me, flying all over my head. I flailed my arms but to no avail. I took a refuge in a phone booth (KX100).

'… please say your name again? Louder and slower!' I said

'ME-AANIE!' Said the TV license phone operator.

'Ok, Me-aanie. You see, I don't watch TV at all, so, why do I have to pay for a TV license?'

'I'm sorry. Anbad who --- a TV ass to pay…'

'I am sorry. I cannot hear you. I live in my own. I cannot ask anybody to call you for me…'

'Im sooy…?

'I cannot afford to pay. I never watch TV. I only watch films. I borrowed money to buy my new TV, so I can watch films in a large screen…'

'YOU CAN pay in monthy…'

'I already pay £10 a month to watch films and you want me to pay for something I never use…'

'I DO NOT THINK I wee b ABLE HELP YOU…'

I slammed the handset on the phone and looked around. I saw hundreds of pigeons, literally, surrounding the phone booth and eating. I then saw a short and fat old man with a large belly and bald head, throwing food around, on the pavement. And when I tried to open the door, the man threw food into the phone booth. Dozens of pigeons entered the booth and began eating around my feet.

I wrote my first short story, The Girl and the Cloud over an existing film script. However, I forgot to delete the words 'THE END' at the end of the short story. This was pointed out to me by a poet friend who told me that you don't write

THE END in stories. This got me thinking, why do we always see the word THE END, written mostly in white on a black background when a film ends. Films don't end with the word THE END on black screen. After THE END, we still think about the film from its last frame and onwards, constructing an epilogue. We go back and forth about what happened and what should or could have happened and what we wished to have happened. In the process, we draw events to our own conclusion, that we may change many times over. So, perhaps there is no beginning either! An artist friend of mine once told me that her white canvas is never empty before she begins to paint. It is already populated with the mind's projections of images.

I got a new digital hearing aid. This hearing aid has a memory. It remembers to distinguish the human voice from the background noise around me. When it does so, it amplifies the voice and softens for example, the sounds in the street. As a result, my friendship with Bef became much closer. I could hear Bef more clearly when I walked with him in the streets and sometimes, I'd tease him and say, 'My hearing aid remembers you better than me.' Hearing through hearing aids is not as straight forward as putting on glasses. Perhaps I could compare it to filming. When shooting a film, recording sound, even on location, is relatively easy, recording images however, is more complicated when it comes to lighting. To simplify the difference in quality, between analogue hearing aids which I had in the past, and digital hearing aids, perhaps we can think of the difference between a VHS Camcorder and an HD camera. No matter how good the HD is, its image is still 2D flat. Some changes are great, some are fine, and some are not, I told myself, standing outside a corner shop after I bought a candle. I looked at The Film Shop, on the other side of the street. I lit the candle and began crossing the street. I struggled with the wind and rain to keep the flame alive. I protected the flame with my hands and my coat. Cars stopped and honked their horn. It took me 9 minutes! I put the candle on the pavement in front of the black door of The Film Shop. The flame died out. The Film Shop was converted to a grocery store and was called Desmond's. But that too, soon closed. I peeped through the horizontal tubes' security shutters. I saw an abandoned ice cream vendor freezer and scattered papers on the floor. I looked at the empty shelves all over the walls, then to my left where I used to stand before the desk and chat to Gabrielle, who stood behind it with her tiny but toned figure, her square-shaped beautiful face with thick red lips that once shouted; Haworth! Village of Haworth! I then looked straight at the flat dark wall with no door that would lead you down after a few steps to the Arthouse room. I was a member of The Film Shop for almost four years. And for two of those years, I used to go down to this room, practically every day, taking home with me three films a day; sometimes four or five, if the staff were in a generous mood. I knew this space so well I told myself, but does it recognise me? Spaces know no mercy. They just spit at your back as soon as you leave them. The relationship is entirely one-sided. Or, perhaps they love us silently. Perhaps that is why they keep dragging us to them, time and again by putting their spell on us, long before we even knew it.

II

Friday Past Midnight.

London, Islington, London, 2009.

On a Friday after midnight, Upper Street is busy with revelers. Negash, a man in his early twenties and looking drunk, walks past two young pretty girls, also seemingly drunk and eating kebabs. The two girls throw a glance at Negash and giggle.

Negash holds a small piece of a paper and stands alone next to a phone booth (KX100). Negash tries to hand the paper to a young passerby who barely throws him a glance. But he manages to stop another young passerby, who reads it, laughs out loud and walks away. Negash hands a £10 note to a homeless middle-aged man, covered in a blanket and holding a dirty worn-out black suitcase who shakes Negash's hands in gratitude. Negash hands him the paper. The homeless man reads it and disappears into the phone booth and emerges a few minutes later, holding a call card.

As Negash looks down at the house number, a young man in a city suite emerges from the basement flat. Negash looks away and walks back. Negash waits until the man disappears from his view, then walks down and rings the bell.

A middle-aged woman opens the door and let Negash in. Negash walks through the entrance room. In the room, there is a woman asleep on a two-seater sofa, covered in a blanket with only her bare feet visible. Another woman is sitting half asleep on a chair, covered to the neck, in front of a TV showing a foreign channel. A young brunette, tall and slightly plump with big breasts walks past Negash. Her body is covered with a large towel and her head is in a shower cap. She is also holding a pair of high heeled shoes in one hand and knickers in the other. The woman puts the shoes and the other items on the floor and sits on the floor next to a radiator.

Negash sits on a double bed. Three girls in lingerie come into the room and stand in front of Negash; one is very young, blonde with tiny figure. Another has short hair and the third is the one he saw earlier wrapped in a towel. The girl with the towel asks Negash which girl he wants. Negash, signing, tells her that he is deaf. The girl switches off the music. Using her fingers, she gestures money. Negash shows her the back of the call card, it reads:

£60 = 30 mins, full service including massage.
£100 = 1hour, full service including massage.
£30 = Blowjob only.

Negash points at £60 and chooses the girl with the towel. When they are alone, Negash drops to his knees and hugs the girl for a long time. The girl, and after a long hesitation, strokes Negash's head gently. The girl hears loud sounds coming from outside. She beacons to Negash to go under the bed and walks out of the room.

One male police officer stands by the main exit door. Two other male officers check documents. The three girls, still in their lingerie, sit on the sofa next to the middle aged woman, who appears to be the madam. A woman officer looks at the madam, and says, 'You are under arrest on suspicion of human trafficking for sexual exploitation...'

In the morning, Negash wakes up and crawls out from under the bed. He opens the flat's door and walks up the stairs slowly. As he pushes the iron bar gate, he sees a young couple who seem to be living in the flat above. They are on their way out for a weekend trip. There are few bags on the pavement next to their Mini and a small dog on the back seat. Among those bags, there is one large brown recyclable Primark bag. Negash puts his head down and walks past the couple. He looks at the gated garden and then at the square's name: Gibson Square.

Notes on the Weather
Chloe Aridjis

Germany: A geometric front stretching east and north from large quadrilaterals centred over Berlin will bring the threat of extreme angularity. Damaging fractals, torrential axioms, and even isolated zeros will be possible from Cologne down into Bavaria.

France: Vigorous symbolism will continue to bring threat of shipwreck and heavy mermaid showers in several locations.

Hungary: A Cimmerian front stretching east and north and giant owls hovering over Budapest will bring a rash of ancestral thunder. Intermittent candlelight, unidentified accents, and even isolated Bluebeards will be possible from Vác down to Hódmezővásárhely.

Mexico: High pressure from underground will create significant craquelure throughout the country. Increased moisture in the south will lead to expansion and contraction depending on temperature. Spiral cracks in the north due to extreme tension on surface, corn ear cracks in the southeast due to sliding pressure. Meanwhile, a white powdery front moves in from the southeast towards the north border.

Russia: A suprematist front will be stretching from northwest to southeast, with heavy abstraction bringing possibility of aesthetic purity. Black spells, chromatic silences, and occasional rain of wolves will be experienced from Saint Petersburg to Vladivostok.

And then there is England, my home. Because I live here the weather feels more prosaic, as do its weather reports. One searches for allegory, but it hides behind a cloud, its signs not readily open to prediction or interpretation, a constant game of chance between the sky and the umbrella. My report, therefore, remains abstract:

England: A strong low poetic system will lead to metaphor and potentially damaging similes across England today. The strongest metaphors will occur on the southwest side, where they could gust past their referents at 60 kph (40 mph). Allegory totals upwards of 2cm can be expected.

Yet once, long ago, the country, or rather my idea of it, represented something more tangible and concrete.

SPEAK AND SPELL

Even the cover was intriguing, and worthy of inquiry: a white swan (real? stuffed? papier mâché?), wrapped in cellophane, perched on a white nest that resembled something like crystallised angel hair pasta. Clearly shot in a studio, the background is a pinkish red, undefinable, unlocatable, warmly synthetic. Nature smothered in plastic or cellulose, yet exuding a strange beauty. The swan is backlit in a peculiar way by some undefined light source, perhaps more than one. We cannot see its eyes since it's tilting its head back a little as if struggling to break free. In the upper right-hand corner reads the band's name in cursive – Depeche Mode – and below, the album's title, SPEAK AND SPELL, in capitals. This was the band's first album, from 1981, the only one graced by Vince Clarke before he went off to form Yazoo and then Erasure. It is also the most pop of Depeche Mode's albums, despite hints of the dark undercurrent of the subsequent ones, the more unrestrained melancholy developed once Martin Gore took over from Clarke as songwriter. The lightness of the synth melodies is offset by Dave Gahan's baritone voice, and the songs have a fantastic buoyancy: 'New Life,' 'Dreaming of Me,' 'Photographic'... to my ears, each was a dialogue between all those stormy and exhilarating adolescent emotions, and to this day whenever I listen to the album I'm thrown back to when I first heard it, a few years after it came out, at age thirteen.

Before I left Mexico to study in the United States and the UK, the English language lived loudly in my head through music. Through literature too, of course, but during my adolescence certain bands provided much of the soundtrack to daily life in Mexico City. Along with Depeche Mode other faithful friends included the Smiths, the Cure, Joy Division, the Sisters of Mercy, Siouxsie and the Banshees, Echo and the Bunnymen, Nick Cave and the Bad Seeds, and The Jesus and Mary Chain. Voices borne on the waves of synthesizers or carried up and down the vertebrae of guitars. I listened to them in my bedroom and in my sister's bedroom, at parties, bars and nightclubs across the city. And beyond the city I listened to them on my Walkman as our family drove down country roads to Contepec, the small village in Michoacán where my grandparents lived, English longing and laments framing the Mexican landscape, foreign shadows dappling the sunlit roads.

In those years my sister and I were best friends with a brother and sister, Carlitos and Natasha Fuentes, who, like us, were the children of a writer. They shared most of our musical and literary tastes and, by extension, a somewhat romanticised view of England. I now realise – only now – that for us England, and London in particular, represented the future, the place where we'd settle as grown-ups and fulfil our dream of becoming whatever we dreamt of becoming. (At the time we had only a vague idea of how miserable most of the population was under Thatcher). We formed a rock group with the new-wave name of No Romance in China, but since it was the name of Vince Clarke's first band, we changed it to Second Scene. We'd stay up all night listening to our favourite albums and watching classic films like *Kind Hearts and Coronets* and read Shelagh Delaney's savage and unique *A Taste of Honey*, on the lookout for lines borrowed by Morrissey. We also put on plays, mainly for ourselves, and filmed them with a clunky Betamax camera. Most of our repertoire was from Oscar Wilde but once we staged Kafka's short story 'The Bridge,' which involved Carlitos buttressed precariously between two chairs. Occasionally we put on musical shows for each set of parents, our only performances in front of a live audience. For the sake of authenticity, most of these home productions involved British accents, although needless to say none of ours came out quite right.

A little over a decade later Carlitos and then Natasha passed away, aged 25 and 30, making those times seem even more dreamlike and ephemeral. My daily life in London is entirely disconnected from that past, at least on a conscious level, yet every now and then I'm reminded with a jolt of our young friends and our reverie-fuelled friendship. As for my sister, after Mexico she moved on to Princeton and then New York (though she did marry an Englishman). So out of our little quartet I was the only one to ultimately make a life in England, though it's a different England from the one of our fantasies. And like the character in Alain-Fournier's *Le Grand Meaulnes* who endlessly tries to revisit an enchanted moment in his adolescence now idealised beyond hope, I'm aware this chapter is destined to grow ever more elusive and opaque, wrapped in more and more layers of cellophane.

Something else we shared with the Fuentes children was a love of animals and the strong sentiment that they should not be killed for food. During the years of our friendship the four of us became vegetarian and would listen, when we could bear it, to the title song of the Smiths' album *Meat is Murder*. Our attachment to England was bolstered by the sense that here was a country where compassion towards animals had a place. When I visited London with my family in the summers of 1987 and 1988 we went to Food for Thought in Neal Street and to Cranks, a vegetarian chain started in the early sixties, and I remember thinking how inspired and ethically ahead of everywhere else they were in their approach to animal welfare. Both places have since closed, Food for Thought only quite recently, yet there are more vegans and vegetarians than ever, especially amongst the younger generation, as people realise that a plant-based food system is the only hope for our planet.

*

THEY HAD NO CHOICE reads an inscription on one side of the Animals in War memorial. A longer inscription, also chiselled into the semi-circle of curved white wall, reads: 'This monument is dedicated to all the animals that served and died alongside British and allied forces in wars and campaigns throughout time.'

The memorial didn't yet exist when I visited as a teen or even during my early years in London, but ever since it appeared I have felt as though it's been forever part of the cityscape, there at a bend at one edge of Hyde Park, at the junction of Park Lane and Upper Brook Street. Other countries have erected memorials to animals that have died in human wars, I know England is not the first, but for me this remains the most stirring landmark in London. Commissioned by the Imperial War Museum, the monument was designed by the British sculptor David Backhouse, and unveiled in late 2004. I had only ever seen it from afar, from the window of a moving car or bus, until the day I went on foot to take these pictures.

The structure is even more affecting from up close, a kind of Noah's Ark in reverse, in which the creatures march towards their doom rather than salvation. There are two levels, divided by a curved white wall that represents the panorama of war. The wall is split in two, suggesting a before and after. On the lower level two bronze mules, laden with heavy equipment, approach the gap with a visible sense of patient resignation. The mule at the front raises its head as if trying to summon up courage for what is to come – on the afternoon I went, it cast a poignant shadow – while the second mule hangs its head in dejection. On the other side of the wall, the raised level supports two more bronze animals, this time a large horse and a dog. The horse gallops off, released, but the dog turns around as if searching for the thousands of comrades who never made it back from the battlefield.

Chiselled into the stone are more animals, a procession of the other species that have also been exploited in our conflicts

– camels, elephants, sheep, cattle, carrier pigeons. On the front of the wall they appear in bas-relief. On the back, their millions of lives now lost, is a ghostly imprint.

It is no mystery that animals are at the service of whatever country they happen to be born in. Their fate, like that of most humans who lack the freedom or the resources to migrate, remains at the mercy of their native land. In an essay I wrote in 2017, I discussed how animals do not have countries, however, but habitats. They forage, gallop, soar across invisible zones imposed by humans, and in doing so their destinies often become entangled with ours. They exist outside of our measurements, except where our spaces overlap, and every geopolitical decision we make, every line drawn through a territory, affects hundreds of species beyond our own. (In 2016 there were several articles about the fences erected along certain borders in Eastern Europe to stem the flow of refugees, and how these were also terrible for local wildlife. More recently, there is real concern for the 111 or so migratory species, including the magnificent jaguar, that live along the US/Mexico border and whose livelihood, even survival, would be seriously threatened by Trump's wall).

London's Animals in War memorial is a rupture in my journey, pulling me out of whatever mood might've been brought on by the rhythms of bus or city. But a powerful memorial does exactly that, it demands a pause; you stop hearing the traffic, are hardly aware of the incessant whirlpool around you. You enter a space of silence, are briefly at one with these doomed animals, and depart with a new heaviness. Yet I am deeply grateful for its existence. It honours the past and feels relevant to the present and, alas, no doubt to the future.

*

As the product of several migrations, there will always be a small nomad within me, and a tendency to feel foreign wherever I am. Not unrelated to my love and concern for animals is the fact I am quick to notice figures in the margins, of whatever species, who seem to exist at the harsh receiving end of society. My maternal grandparents were Jews from Russia, Poland and Lithuania who emigrated to the United States in the late nineteenth century. My paternal grandfather was a Greek from Smyrna, who after fighting the Turks in 1922 departed for Brussels and in 1926 went on to Mexico, where he settled. My Mexican grandmother was the daughter of a Spaniard.

Despite this family history of migrations, it was only when I moved to England that I officially fell into the category of migrant, and was labelled as one for the first time. Over the years I have inhabited this country in various guises: first on a student visa, while I did my M.Phil. and D.Phil. Then, once I'd published my first novel and moved back from Berlin, I was granted a visa as a Highly Skilled Migrant Tier 1. After five years as a resident I was granted 'indefinite leave to remain,' which means permanent residency as well as the freedom to practice any profession – except for medicine, or sports presenting (to avoid possible partiality?) – and finally, in September 2016, I became a British citizen. Despite the odd sensation of holding a British passport with my very un-British name on it, I felt in some ways as though I had become a citizen long ago.

Borders, frontiers: impermanent by nature, always subject to re-drawing and negotiation. To many they remain invisible, until the day arrives, perhaps, when they no longer are[1]. For a long time, despite the frequency with which I moved about, they felt abstract to me too. Until my first – and most direct – encounter with the iron-clad hand of immigration, that is, which took place fifteen years ago, just as I was finishing my D.Phil at Oxford. Early one morning in June 2002 the postman rang the bell to deliver an envelope from the Home Office. *Please leave the country within ten working days*, read the letter. My student visa was about to expire, so goodbye. In a few lines typed out by a clerk, my entire existence in the United Kingdom was thrown into doubt, the carpet pulled from under me.

I had built a life for myself here and intended to stay on after my graduate studies. What I didn't know when filling out my application was that the Home Office harboured a particular dislike, and seeming mistrust, of students who attempted to remain. After your studies, unless perhaps you were going

---

1   In *Species of Spaces* (1974) Georges Perec describes it with beautiful simplicity: 'Countries are divided from one another by frontiers. Crossing a frontier is quite an emotive thing to do: an imaginary limit, made material by a wooden barrier which as it happens is never really on the line it purports to represent, but a few dozen or hundreds of meters this side or that of it, is enough to change everything, even the landscape. It's the same air, the same earth, but the road is no longer quite the same, the writing on the road signs changes, the baker's shops no longer look altogether like the thing we were calling a baker's shop just a short while earlier, the loaves are no longer the same shape, there are no longer the same cigarette packets lying around on the ground.' It is with a certain nostalgia that one reads these lines about a now obsolete notion, that of an invisible limit between countries, drawn but not demarcated, in which one searches for subtle cultural signs as the only evidence of geographical shift.

to contribute towards the nation's bank account with a hefty investment or a promising career in finance, you were expected to kindly depart. After seven years in the country, with nearly all of my friends British, I had practically forgotten that I lived here on other terms, that my residency, unlike theirs, was tenuous, and never to be taken for granted. And because my oral exam fell within those ten working days – I'd handed in my dissertation and this was all that was needed to complete my degree – the university could not intervene on my behalf. *Please leave the country within ten working days...* Years later, those words continued to haunt me.

So, I took my exam and flew back to my house in Mexico, and one month later re-entered the United Kingdom on a tourist visa. It was disconcerting to return as a visitor to the place that up until then had felt unequivocally like home. All signs pointed towards change. That December, I packed up my flat and in early 2003 moved to Berlin.

*

Why Berlin? My family and I had spent the summers of 1986 and 1988 there, when my father had been a guest of the DAAD artists exchange programme and been given a large flat near the Kurfürstendamm. Each day we went for long walks and visited a museum. Most evenings we'd go see outlandish circus and theatre productions. The flow of input and inspiration was pretty much constant and the city cast such a spell, I knew I would return. What I didn't know, of course, was that I would be returning to a changed city, no longer divided, engaged in the complicated process of redefining itself. But on a personal level so was I, and the years I spent in Berlin would prove vital to my development as a writer.

In writing about one city you nearly always evoke another, the one you left behind, the city destined to remain the alter ego of the one you ultimately chose to dwell in. That 'other city' represents all the spaces you could've inhabited but didn't. At first, there is an ongoing conversation between the city of your past and the city of your present. On a recent trip to Berlin I walked past my old building, at Chodowieckistraße 37[2], and experienced a certain vertigo as I drew near my former home. I glanced up at the fourth floor, noted the different curtains, preferred not to know more. It was strange to think that all of my belongings, that very particular configuration of books, objects and furniture belonging to one Chloe Aridjis, had now been transferred to London, and in that space nothing of me remained, not a trace, no residual mark apart from perhaps a few scratches in the wooden floor left when the movers hauled away the heavy sofa or the bookshelves; the current inhabitants would have no inkling of my existence, similarly unaware of my figure standing on the pavement peering up at the windows.

In London my things, or rather, certain things, have a different aura than they did in Berlin. They are no longer rubbing up against their pasts, have lost some of their charge, have indeed been reduced to the status of things. I am talking about the furniture and objects that I bought over the five and a half years I lived there.

2   Daniel Chodowiecki: an eighteenth century Polish artist, primarily of drawings and engravings – East Berliners pronounced his surname the Polish way, West Berliners the German way. A cab driver's provenance, as well as a passenger's, could usually be guessed by their pronunciation.

I acquired nearly everything at flea markets, where I'd make the rounds most Sundays, either Arkonaplatz or Boxhagener Platz and then, towards the end of my time, the Mauerpark flea market, which grew and grew along a grassy strip where the Wall once ran, the once-divided ground now colonised by seas of knickknacks all tossed together, boxes full of two-euro crockery and candlesticks, antique chairs and dressers – a grand accumulation of things, multiplying from week to week, for waves of eager scavengers to sift through.

That was Berlin, however. London objects tend to lack historical frisson; a visit to a flea market doesn't offer vestiges of a recently defunct nation, no obsolete phone books or printed badges and crockery. What here would possess the same allure, I wondered – relics from Victorian London? At a little antique market near my house I came across an orphaned object that seemed to possess that sought-after sheen of the past: a miniature brass Victorian boot once used to strike matches on its sole. Black with a gold-plated cuff, it is a sturdy little piece of footwear that I like to imagine went on many travels through the nineteenth-century city, tucked into a pocket rather than trudging the pavement, en route, perhaps, to different drinking holes. Or perhaps it was nicked and passed on from hand to hand, part of the hidden currency circulated in dark alleyways. The metal is rippled to imitate folds in leather and the sides are genuinely scuffed as if by wear. It cost me twenty pounds, which given its age seemed reasonable, and now sits on a bookshelf at home, silent and stilled, far from any pocket, pavement or matches. If the past is a foreign country, I wonder whether it is doubly foreign if it concerns the past of a country that is not your own. Yet this is the wonder of miniatures: they contain a whole universe within, space and time collapsed into their tiny frames, and in owning one, you come into magical possession of the world they embody.

*

Not long ago I was asked to contribute to a spirited anthology called *An Unreliable Guide to London* (Influx Press, 2016). Each writer was to invent a place within the city, or else take an actual place and recast it in a new light. My entry envisioned the capital and particularly N1, where I live, as a place of illusion in which certain corners and junctions are the site of extraordinary optical tricks, most likely due to the way light particles interact with specific architectural features:

Two main categories of optical illusion have been established: those produced on land, and those produced on water. Thanks to the canal that runs through much of the borough, elements of this latter category have been seen to flourish. Some Islington residents for instance have proven more receptive to reflections on hard surfaces while others are specifically attuned to reflections on water.

As for the reflections spotted on the canal in N1, these include glitter patterns, wake patterns and cat's paws. Glitter patterns are ensembles of sun glints, instantaneous flashes of sunlight reflected for a moment on a sloping wave and then gone. The canal is especially abundant with cat's paws, which are dark regions of water where the wind touches down and tenses the surface.

On land, meanwhile, one of the most widely noted shadow appearances, for those in search of such things, has been that of the Brocken Spectre, looming three-dimensional shadows cast onto buildings, especially in times of fog. There have been sightings of a Golem silhouette, meanwhile, slinking across the old Carlton cinema in Essex Road and smaller versions across the exterior of the Charles Lamb pub after closing time. Other buildings nearby have also been brushed by large unexpected shadows. Night, the great muralist.

By now I've realised that this is how I operate: I map out a place, search for ways to defamiliarize, add in a few ambiguous Gothic motifs... London isn't as overtly mysterious as Berlin, nor does it possess the same toolbox of tensions, but it is of course just as layered.

For my first novel, *Book of Clouds,* I wandered Berlin with my notebook, studying the faces of people on public transport and lingering in certain areas of the city that triggered a creative form of unease. For my second novel I was back in London and conducted a somewhat different kind of investigation. In the early days of researching *Asunder,* whose narrator is a female museum guard at the National Gallery, I drew up a list of ten questions and would tentatively approach warders in different art galleries. My curiosity was mostly to do with their daily routines, and their degree of attachment to the art all around them. I also asked about invisibility – and to my surprise, every single reply indicated a preference to remain unnoticed. No one wanted their existence acknowledged when visitors entered the room they were watching over.

Luckily for me, the chattiest individuals happened to be the ones who worked at the National Gallery. They described their daily routine and pulled out their personalised charts to explain the logistics of room rotation. The man in the archives kindly provided me with the historical minutes of the gallery. The guards at the British Museum, however, were only allowed to answer questions pertaining to the collection – for reasons of security, they added. At the Serpentine I encountered art students for the most part; they gave familiar and predictable answers, and were therefore less illuminating. And at Tate Britain, I had a startling exchange – in retrospect, very British – with a guard seated in the room where hung Edward Burne-Jones's 21 foot-long painting 'The Last Sleep of Arthur in Avalon,' occupying an entire wall (on loan briefly from the Museo de Arte de Ponce in Puerto Rico). For several uncomfortable minutes I found myself within that odd triangulation of guard–visitor–painting, and stood contemplating the soulful work before finally turning to the man in his chair behind me. Busy applying chapstick to his lips, he didn't quite smile when I approached. I timidly inquired whether I could ask him a few questions for a book I was writing. 'Absolutely not!' he replied in a huff, 'I refuse to be the subject of a writer's imagination!' And with that, the interview was adjourned before it had even begun.

My Private Prime Meridian

Zinovy Zinik

You cannot cross the same city twice.

Psychologists tell us, that if, having entered a room, you suddenly realise that you cannot recollect what you have come in for, you should retreat to the point of departure, outside that room, and retrace your steps to enter the same room again for the second time in order to remember the purpose of your first entry.

My first entry to London was a very baffling experience. I reached the British shore forty years ago, arriving in Dover on a ferry boat from Calais. In the early morning fog, even the badly signed path round the fence of the ferry port that led to the train station was not easy to follow. Let alone to find out where any of the trains go to, and from which platform they depart. Passengers had to watch a mechanical display closely, in which little tablets indicating each train's destination were turning, not always in sync with other little tablets indicating the departure platforms, which would again turn and change not in sync with those little tablets in which the time of departure would constantly change depending on the state of affairs on the railway line plagued by disruptions of different kinds and causes of which at that time I could not comprehend.

The old railway carriages looked like the set of cabins on the channel ferry, each cabin supplied with its own door. At the approaches to London, I saw through the soot and grime of my train window a juxtaposition of railway bridges and byways over the miles of terraced houses, each with its front door, that also looked like passenger cabins of a ship or, again, like the carriages of a very long train moving through the sea fog. That reminded me yet again that I've arrived in the country that once had ruled the waves.

Luckily, I landed safely on the Charing Cross station platform. At the ticket barrier, I asked a jolly railway official how to find my way to the British Broadcasting Corporation where I was expected as a new recruit. He took a fat metal whistle out of his mouth (the whistle was used to regulate train departures) and explained to me, in detail, naming street after street, how to cross the West End from Trafalgar Square to Oxford Circus and reach Broadcasting House at Langham Place, off Upper Regent Street. I was even told that I would recognise the building by the sculpture of Prospero and Ariel of Shakespeare's *Tempest* on its facade. At the entrance to Prospero's establishment I was informed that there were two BBCs in town and that I had been expected not in the Broadcasting House but at Bush House, which was located in Covent Garden, not very far from the Charing Cross railway station from which I had started my search. That meant I had to retrace my steps by crossing the West End again. I had to cross the square mile of Soho for the second time before it dawned on me that I had been passing through the legendary part of London familiar to me only from novels.

The difference between BBC two premises was symbolic. The Broadcasting House was known as the BBC Home Service, the radio station for those who lived in Britain, those who regarded Britain as their home, and who were mainly British. While Bush House, known as the World Service, was designated as the Overseas or External Services of the BBC, engaged in external broadcasting – for those British who lived outside Britain or for foreigners; that is, for the rest of the world. The World Service was the station that used to broadcast in scores of languages, incorporating all the former British Empire nationalities. Broadcasters, recruited from every corner of the world, had populated the convoluted corridors of Bush House. It was initially called The BBC Empire Service and it was indeed a symbolic miniature model of the British Empire in a single building. In the entrance hall, the head of an ancient Roman was exhibited (it had been dug up at the foundation pit when Bush House was built in the late 1920s). In short, Bush House was a recreation of the British Empire on the radio waves and my voice had extended this radio empire to include Russia. In this division of broadcasting into two categories - external and internal - I had eventually recognised a metaphoric manifestation of the duality that intrinsic to every émigré existence. My body was in the West while its twain, my voice, in the East. In my broadcasts I had been talking to people whom I never saw about things that they would never be able to see. An ideal situation for the fiction writer.

That Cartesian duality caused me to perceive symbolically some topographical aspects of London that for the native Londoner might have always been just a hackneyed mundane fact of the city's history. One example was the Prime Meridian which I 'discovered' when, for different family reasons, I had moved from Hampstead to Lewisham - a place highly recommended to me by my good friend and an experienced Londoner, Prof. Alexander Piatigorsky, who had been a denizen of Lewisham for some time. A lecturer at the School of Oriental Studies at the University of London, Piatigorsky was older than me for two decades; he had become a kind of mentor for me during the first years of my London life.

South London is hardly distinguishable from the county of Kent and I'm sure I already crossed the Prime Meridian once, during my first journey across Kent from Dover to London. Looking out of the train window, I couldn't at that time possibly notice that I had been crossing the imaginary line that runs across the globe from the North Pole to the South Pole. Neither had I been I aware that in one of those unremarkable rows of houses that I saw from the train window there was the house of Prof. Piatigorsky, a prominent Buddhist scholar, who would become my long-standing neighbour and interlocutor.

Forty years ago, not yet a British subject who had been stripped of his Russian citizenship for his decision to leave forever his Soviet motherland, I was desperate to define the sense of my homelessness with words and images when the Iron Curtain was still a divisive reality. It was during the one of our long strolls with Prof. Piatigorsky through the nearby Greenwich Park that I had arrived at the conclusion that we could understand what we had really suffered from in our motherland only by crossing the border and settling down in a foreign country. Visiting Greenwich Observatory for the first time, I experienced a kind of semantic serendipity by straddling the piece of rail called the Prime Meridian - with one foot in the East and another in the West.

Such a symbolic conceptual division of the world is too tempting to resist exploiting ideologically. No wonder that in the novel *The Secret Agent* by Joseph Conrad, the idea of blowing up of the Royal Greenwich Observatory by an anarchist double agent is concocted by the Russian Embassy in London: the aim is to exploit the fear of anarchism among the British public and provoke the reactionary clampdown on every liberal political movement in Britain and all over Europe. Dilemmas posed by anarchism - in our choosing between liberty and social order - were taken quite personally by Conrad.

Among his contemporaries was the spiritual father of anarchism Prince Peter Kropotkin, the darling of liberal London circles. Kropotkin lived not very far from the Prime Meridian - in Bromley - and as a great revolutionary cartographer he was a honourable guest of the Royal Geographical Society. Conrad, a Pole by blood, was born in a Ukrainian Jewish town of Berdychiv, but grew up in the Northern Russia where his father, a Polish patriot, was exiled by the Tsarist government. Although a sworn enemy of the Russian autocracy, Conrad, unlike Kropotkin, abhorred the revolutionary violence of any kind. That's how topography of London got intertwined in my mind, influenced by Joseph Conrad, with the history of Russian authoritarianism, anarchism, and my own troublesome past of an immigrant.

Once you start following a certain intriguing line in one's life's narrative, it is very difficult to deviate from it. The death of some enemies of the Russian government a century later, by a poisoned umbrella on Waterloo Bridge or by a radioactive tea in South Kensington, had become part of the same plot. The arrival in London of Russian oligarchs, some of whom had once been the KGB employees and now become the owners of corporate enterprises and masters of surreal fortunes, has only boosted the topicality of Conrad's novel. If there is anything that Russian expats are united by, it is definitely the fear of the Russian government and its double agents.

I thought that since I had lost my Russian citizenship years ago, I got rid of this fear. Up to a point. In the 1970s, Russians were as rare on the streets of London as, at that time, croissants in corner shops. Good four years had passed after my arrival in England before I heard for the first time the sound of Russian spoken outside the BBC Russian Service. I lived temporarily in the district of Chelsea ominously called World's End (Beckett once stayed there and didn't like it, neither did I), and one day, while walking along High Street Kensington, I suddenly heard behind my back a sentence in Russian, measured as rhythmically as the toll of Kremlin's clock tower:

'Time's up for Ivan Ivanovich'. This statement was quite hair-raising, even intimidating - not only because of its content, but because I didn't expect to hear Russian words spoken in the middle of a London street. I'd cast a quick furtive glance behind and saw two awkward bulky guys in Fedora hats and badly tailored suits, evidently employees of the Soviet Embassy nearby. I was in a panic: should I report to the nearest police station on the imminent demise of a certain citizen Ivan Ivanovich; or should the idiomatic 'time's up' be interpreted simply as a termination of his diplomatic career in London? But these contradictory feelings were upstaged by the overwhelming sensation of hearing my native tongue in a foreign city. Amazingly, these two Russians behind my back somehow assumed that there was nobody around to understand their bizarre barbaric lingo. There had been so few of us around in those days.

Had they known there was a native Russian speaker nearby, they would have kept their mouths shut. So would have I, had I noticed a compatriot in the vicinity. It was fear of one's own identity, stemming from a sense of shame for your country's political past or present. I'm sure this feeling is familiar not only to Russians – I've seen Americans and Germans behaving the same way, Jews and Arabs know it, too. It takes some psychological self-training not to feel slightly embarrassed each time when my Russian origin is exposed in the company of the Brits.

Not that there are many of us left who would feel embarrassed. London is now swarming with the new generation of Russians who have cast away the shackles of their totalitarian past and are not tied up by the dubious political bonds in the present. They flaunt their Russianness unashamedly. It had become evident to me for the first time two decades ago when the then mayor of London, Ken

Livingstone, provided Trafalgar Square free of charge for the public celebration in London of the Russian New Year, according to the Old Style Julian calendar. Ken Livingstone had been very much enchanted by Russians. Having expelled the pigeons from the square, Red Ken invited his beloved Russian oligarchs and expats to transform the place that commemorates the Battle of Trafalgar into a simulacrum of the Red Square. Russian food stalls, souvenir tents and vodka kiosks had been put up on the perimeter of the *platz*. Thousands of Russians and their British cronies were pressed together around Nelson's Column, each (apart from Nelson) talking without any inhibitions in Russian on mobile phones, locating their mates' parallels and meridians lost in the crowd, their mobile ringtones drowning ill-adjusted loud speakers for the gala concert in front them. It was a show of state-sponsored expat nostalgia - a predictable jolly mix of Chechen dancers, folk singers, pop-groups of old romantics, a marching unit of the imported Kremlin guards and the Red Army State Choir. Over the heads of the cheerful crowd, a huge balloon in the windy sky advertising Aeroflot services had been slapping the monumental Nelson in the face, as if punishing him for standing aloof amidst the democratic festivities. A huge ice model of St. Basil's Cathedral of the Red Square was erected in the corner, slowly melting and symbolising the ending of the cold war.

While I was observing this boisterous Russian spectacle, I had suddenly heard behind my back a sentence in Russian, as well-measured rhythmically as the toll of Big Ben: 'Time's up for Feodor Feodorovich'. I cast a glance behind. There stood two bulky gentlemen in tracksuits and Puma trainers – no Fedora hats anywhere around. That day on

Trafalgar Square, there were more foreigners in Russian fur hats than Russians in American baseball caps. But certain national features never change. The voice behind my back had become slightly more mature with the years, no doubt, but it was still the same voice – I can assure you of this as a professional broadcaster. It was a confident voice, of the new free and democratic Russia where there was no place for Ivan Ivanovich, Feodor Feodorovich and such like. The voice, perhaps, was only in my head. And yet I decided to pretend I didn't understand Russian. Just in case.

The memory of these ominous pronouncements on the fate of Ivan Ivanovich and Feodor Feodorovich rings a bell totally different from that of 'Time's up!' shouted obligatory in the past by publicans when the last drink was about to be served before the bar's closure, according to the old licensing laws in England. That cry would be usually followed by 'Good night, gentlemen, good night, sweet ladies, ta ta.' The Defence of the Realm Act of August 1914 that forced pubs to shut their doors for three hours in the afternoon, to sustain sobriety at the time of the war, had continued to operate - to the consternation of foreigners and tourists - until the late 1980s. I used to regard these licensing restrictions on the sale of alcohol in London as fatalistically as I had done in regards to the Soviet communism doctrine in my school days. The discovery of private drinking clubs of Soho was like the fall of the Iron Curtain. Behind it, there was a labyrinth of dimly lit entrances that had lead into the magic world hidden to outsiders.

I stumbled into that world as a result of one of my not unusual faux pas in conversations with the grand and famous for my radio show *West-End* at the BBC

Russian Service. In the late 1980s, my friend James Birch, an art dealer, managed to set up a major retrospective of Francis Bacon in Moscow, just before the final collapse of communism. Francis Bacon accused me of undermining this forthcoming exhibition by asking him wrong, provocative questions. During my interview, I flippantly asked him about the symbolic significance of the swastika in one of Bacon's *Crucifixions.* I had in mind the Soviet obsession with the memory of patriotic wars and hence their sensitivity to Fascist symbols; but hysterical, cunning and sometimes paranoid Bacon had perceived my question as a political manoeuvre – an attempt to expose his masochistic fondness for Nazi paraphernalia and push him, a homosexual arch-anarchist, into the camp of anti-Soviet right-wingers of the BBC World Service subsidised by the Foreign Office - a step which would have seriously damaged his reputation in Soviet Russia. Libertarians are sometimes very censorious. He demanded that the recording be stopped.

It was a tête-à-tête conversation and no time limit set: there were only two of us in the empty Marlborough gallery with a bottle of whisky Famous Grouse between us. I switched off my recording machine. To reassure Bacon that I was not an *agent provocateur*, I related a few amusing stories about my departure from Russia, the schizophrenic nature of my life in Moscow and how my life in London had become split into the East and the West by the zero meridian of my emigration from the Soviet Union. Those days Soho was still an asylum for cranky Marxists, champagne anarchists and Trotskyite sadomasochists. In The French House pub one of the regulars was dressed and made up as a Lenin's double. There had been, no doubt, some moments in my life when I wish I could blow up the ideological fiction of the Iron Curtain with the same dark enthusiasm as was once applied by the anarchists to the Prime Meridian.

My convoluted metaphorical parallels had cheered Bacon considerably and he reciprocated with a set of tall tales about his adolescent years in Ireland among stable boys, and under his father's whip, his love for Mayakovsky and for the horrific cinematic image of Eisenstein's shouting nanny with a pram on the Odessa steps. When the bottle of Famous Grouse was done, I was invited to join him and James Birch in the legendary green room in Dean Street.

The Colony Room Club was one of the private drinking joints that would serve thirsty Soho diehards during afternoon hours when the pubs were closed for a break. When Gaston Berlemont, the publican of The French House would trumpet at full throat his 'Time's up, ladies and gentlemen!', those in the know would walk a few doors up the same Dean Street and climb the stairs into the tiny bar of the Colony Room. Created in 1948 by the clever and sharp-tongued Jewish lesbian from Birmingham, Muriel Belcher, it was painted green from top to bottom, and crammed with dusty memorabilia, framed and unframed fragments of the art and life of mutual friends and their sworn enemies.

In the Colony, newcomers had to learn to leave the garments of their social and artistic status behind the doors and to be immune to occasional verbal abuse, which was used as a kind of litmus test to your anarchist credentials. It was anarchism on the personal level where bombs were made of emotions. When I walked through the green door for the first time thirty years ago and was introduced to the former owner, the late Ian Board (whose nose looked like a rotten beetroot and was no doubt an inspiration to the palette of Bacon in later years), I was immediately greeted by him as 'Miss Russia'. When someone, in an attempt to imitate Ian, called me 'Mr Russia', I had enough wit to reply that I had not yet had a sex operation. Everyone laughed and after that Ian stopped treating me as a stranger. In Soho people do ask you what's your origin and where did you come from, but they don't actually care for the answer unless they themselves have a story to tell you about your ancestors. And, regardless of your answer, they'll treat you as one of the family - if they like you. The family here is that of heavy drinkers: that's why displaced persons are so fond of bars.

Soho liberates those who are overburdened with their class or ethnic origins. One day I got fed up with telling again and again to casual encounters the tale of my dramatic departure from the Soviet Union forty years ago. Bored, I decided to introduce myself as the son of a Russian terrorist whose mother was a Jewish Palestinian prostitute. I could demonstrate my fluent Russian and Hebrew as my credentials. Nobody ever bothered to ask for any - they were intrigued by the story regardless of its authenticity. In this, I just followed the examples of a number of remarkable Soho's old timers such as Molly Parkin.

A member of the Colony Room, an octogenarian painter, artiste-pornographer, songwriter and memoirist, with a turban-like construction that adorns her heavily made-up face, Molly tells us in her recent volume of memoirs, that she, too, was a friend of Francis Bacon. Bacon never painted her portrait. She was unable to sit as a model, for him or any other artist, she said, because she is too fidgety. But she and

Bacon finished quite a few bottles of champagne together. She was an intimate friend of the jazz singer and connoisseur of surrealism George Melly, as well. When Molly saw him for the last time just before he died four years ago, he drew the blanket off his bed, saying (in Molly's words), 'Let's embrace each other for old time's sake, while it lasts'. It must be said that Melly at the end of his life was suffering from memory loss. He joked that Alzheimer's brought him a new friendly face every day. Molly also tells us about a brief encounter, backstage, with Louis Armstrong, during one of his London performances. Since all these old friends are now dead, who can confirm what had exactly happened between Molly, Melly and others on this or that occasion? Especially when there were no witnesses. In short, Molly's swinging memoirs liberate everyone's imagination when it comes to our own real or fictional hobnobbing with the grand and famous who are no longer with us. I even had an idea of regular guided tours through Soho, explaining to foreign tourists what and where Francis Bacon ate, drunk and puked and how did he manage to fuck both Freud and Karl Marx. The charm of it is that nobody in Soho would care a toss of exposing you as a bullshitter.

That charming world of secret rendezvous with illicit sex encounters, malicious gossip, amazing confessions and outrageous gestures seemed to have been over when the strict licensing laws had eventually been repealed. Everything has become open and accessible to everyone, democratic and tasteless. It's getting unrecognizable, they say. Indeed, when I first visited Soho, I had to go through badly lit streets with the tall pyramids of rubbish bags around lamp posts and packs of rats under your feet, due to the general strike of dustmen. Later I was told that all these unpleasantries were manifestations of the 'winter of discontent' that had reached Soho more or less at the same time as I did, bringing about with it the waves of strikes, social unrest, vandalism and even upsurge of terrorism.

By that time, I had accepted this all as a hilarious anarchic face of the true capitalism. Nowadays, you have to find your way through the labyrinth of building sites surrounded by corrugated fences. Instead of garishly painted girls in fishnet stockings at the entrances to porn shops, there are gangs of builders in protective helmets on the scaffoldings and naked to their belly buttons, posing to salivate the thirsty mouths of gay men gawping at them. Porn shops look like ethnic museums, striptease theatres are banned in favour of gay sex clubs. The sex industry has gone digital, intimate secrets become electronic. The notions of intimacy are turned inside out. Once Soho was dark and dangerous, now it is all neon-lit, demonstratively transgenderous and multicultural, swanky and organic, more laptops and coffee cups around rather than beer and whisky glasses. Old bars and quaint buildings are destroyed to give way to high-rise apartment blocks for Indian, Chinese and Russian oligarchs. The pubs are packed with noisy crowds of tourists and loutish lads from suburbia. The music in such places is so loud and horrible that only expletives are heard. The gloomy and sceptical Sohoites prophesied the end to the good old Soho.

And yet, those who are desperate to find asylum from this contemporary hell, still have a chance to press the bell of the last door at the southern end of Dean Street and dive downstairs to Gerry's, a private drinking club (of which I'm an honorary member). In good old days, when the Colony

Room's barman would finish serving drinks as the clock stroke eleven, those regulars who still stood on their feet would all flock in here. Michael Dillon the proprietor never minds me bending his ear with yet another brief episode in the long history of the destruction of Soho. 'But it's always been like that,' he muses. 'Buildings are built to be destroyed to be built again. Human beings are the same. Destroyed and then born again. Think of Jesus Christ. Have a drink.' And after a couple of drinks you feel you are again in the same old place, all coloured depressingly brown and billiard green - the favourite palette of the 1950s London.

My Soho's routes are still the same. Soho has changed, but after a trip abroad, I feel I haven't yet arrived back in London until I popped in for a drink at the French House and savoured my double Famous Grouse with a pound sterling of discount granted for old timers and former members of the Colony Room. My little Academy club had changed the location since the time when its original founder Auberon Waugh hosted the launch of my first collection of short stories *One-Way Ticket*, but its contemporary premises - a room over Andrew Edmunds' restaurant - still buzzes friendly with the chattering of literati whose faces unknown to me yet looking familiar. And when everything's closed, you can still find a good company with a wild saxophonist at Trisha's - with its shabby chic of plastic tables with oil tablecloth and shaky chairs that looked the same as I saw it decades ago when it had been an innocuous gambling den for retired businessmen and pensioners of the Italian origin. People come and go, but the type of Soho habitué as a biological specimen remains the same. And the place is still a Babylonian hive of voices, old and new.

Each visit to Soho used to enrich my vocabulary as if you had a trip into another country to which people migrate from the commonplace mundane world of conventionality. This country has its own map, its own routes of navigation secretly shared among the members of this or that drinking clan. Even newly opened places are not entirely disconnected with the old ones. Recently I was invited to the downstairs room called Friendly Society - a jolly gay bar at the corner of Wardour Street and Tisbury Court. On the top floor of the building opposite, my good friend Marina used to live. Her guests, standing on her roof terrace, were occasionally entertained by lonely individuals' masturbation sessions seen through the windows across the street, although all striptease joint downstairs had been officially closed for some time now. When the darkness fell, the secret doors into clandestine worlds with innocuous signs used to create its own matrix of parallels and meridians, guiding the old timers between these watering holes as if they were conducting some shuttle diplomacy with the secret mission.

There are cities, such as Paris or New York, that look like their postcards, whose visage corresponds in reality to the image of them you had in advance constructed in your mind. London is not like anything you'd imagined it to be, because the moment the image got fixed in your mind, it would get changed. More than that, it's gradually dawned on me that there is no such a thing as the single city called London - there are many Londons, towns within towns with worlds within worlds. London is like a Russian doll. But it is not a single Russian doll, there were many. You destroy one and discover another one inside.

Those who regard the old Soho as dead are now crossing the river, to Vauxhall or Kennington, because it is in South London - SoLo - that the real Soho is to be found. Or so they say. The map of London is getting redrawn all the time. Perhaps every district of London must have its own little Soho (like every town with canals has its own Little Venice). There is SoHo in New York. That brings us back to the conception of the Prime Meridian. I'd studied its history and learnt that once upon a time every civilised country had its own Prime or Zero Meridian - the most essential element of cartography. The Greenwich Meridian had eventually won the day because Britain had ruled the waves; the British maps turned out to be the best and as such were accepted by the rest of the world. From time to time, as soon as a new equipment is discovered allowing to gauge the distance from the centre of the earth in a more precise way, the virtual Prime Meridian is being slightly moved, to the east or to the west of its original position.

Inevitably, I'd made another step and concluded that each of us must have our own private Prime Meridian, as it were, around which our inner cartography is constructed. We, as individuals, also have our own matrix of meridians and parallels, rooted in our private experience, to navigate us through life. Sometimes it is linked to our childhood, our parental home. We even position the furniture in a new house in the same configuration as before. And when we move to a new town, to a new quarter of town, we are looking to settle down in a place whose location is in correspondence with that inner map. That inner cartography, these internal, sometimes very emotional set of coordinates, is imposed upon the objective geographical map. The inner cartography sometimes dramatically clashes with and sometimes corresponds to the official map of London.

These two maps are rarely identical. Only stupid politicians imagine the map of the world to be totally identical to their own inner one - because they have none. Others have only a vague memory of the street of their childhood, lost in the kaleidoscope of their round-the-world travels. One way or the other we are trying to juxtapose our nostalgic geography with the real one; and if they clash, our sense of wellbeing is disturbed, undermined. We are looking for an ideal match, wondering around the world in search of it, guided by our inner compass.

Every underground street crossing in London has its own East and West, North and South, which always causes me hesitate a little before I climb the stairs into the street, never certain on which side of the globe I'll find myself. Arriving at Charing Cross station on the train from South London to West End, and crossing the Strand underpath, I had to take east on my way to Bush House. Charing Cross Road that goes north, up to Camden, has become in my mind a kind of Prime Meridian, with the BBC in the East and Soho in the West. (Interestingly, Prof.Piatigorsky had never crossed Charing Cross Road with me in my meandering between Soho bars beyond China Town. He had always remained inside the borders of his mental East.)

I read somewhere that the Irish poet Seamus Heaney would change his drink from Jameson whiskey to Bushmill each time he crossed the border with Northern Ireland. In Soho my favourite tipple was the Famous Grouse. In Covent Garden it was a vodka drink that I had invented some years ago in my usual watering hole PJ's Bar & Grill. That bar was a remarkable mirror version of the World Service located across the road (Aldwych). It'd been patronized by all language services of the BBC. The motley crowd was entertained by Tony, the genius of the place. People try to impose on you the tribal, class, ethnic and religious affinities, want to identify you as a part of a collective, myth, mythology. The BBC World Service taught me how deceptive theses national stereotypes are.

Our foreign accent is a traitor to our cosmopolitan soul striving to remain anonymous in our search for the new life in a foreign land. You open your mouth in a crowd and immediately the question pops up: 'Where're you from?' And you have to explain anew your old life story. But it has never come to anyone's mind to inquire about Tony's origin. Professor Higgins would have abandoned his tutelage of Eliza Doolittle (whom he met, according to George Bernard Shaw, not very far from PJ's) for a chance to spend an hour in Tony's company, because Tony, who had arrived in Britain from Algeria, has an uncanny ability to speak what appears to be every language on earth - and his vocabulary is immense, bearing in mind contributions from foreign employees of the BBC World Service. My contribution was not only verbal. One night, when I had to kill my hangover, I longed for a vodka drink. A traditional Russian shot of vodka, followed by a piece of salted herring on buttered rye bread, was too exotic for this establishment; and I detest vodka cocktails with coke or tonic. So I came up with a simple and ingenious compromise, which I named, after my initials, Double Z.

Fill a tumbler glass generously with ice cubes, pour double vodka over the ice, then squeeze and drop in two wedges of fresh lime. Double Z is to be shaken (twice), not stirred, so your palate is hit now by pure vodka, now by a pungent streak of lime, all mellowed by ice. Refreshing, dramatic and invigorating, the drink is easily consumed and at the same time amazingly effective. Tony was eager to publicize my drink at every opportunity. My rise to fame was swift. I was honoured with the highest distinction that the management can grant to its patrons: a miniature bronze plaque with my name as an honourable regular had been fixed to the bar. The crowd of admirers grew every day.

One night my drink attracted the attention of the middle-eastern-looking man standing next to me. He liked it. We ordered another round. A conversation ensued from which it emerged that my interlocutor was an Iraqi émigré. In outward appearance he resembled a small shopkeeper from that region: outsized potbelly, fleshy nose, permanent stubble. Yet, strictures of Islam aside, his manner of consuming vodka was that of an old hand. In response to my comment he joked that it was wine Mohammed had outlawed, while the Koran made no mention of vodka. Not mentioned – therefore permitted.

Not long before that visit to the bar I had chanced to watch with Prof.Piatigorsky a television documentary about Baghdad and the Iraqi intelligentsia. I was expecting something along the lines of Saudi Arabia, where hands are chopped off for petty theft, and public floggings are meted out for a shot of vodka. Not a bit of it. What I saw was far more akin to Moscow of the Brezhnev era: cafes nestling among enormous prefab housing estates, cavernous, smoke-filled apartments, noisy kitchen-table soirees of dissident intellectuals arguing over coffee-table tomes on Picasso and Bosch and exchanging Camus and Sartre novels. I was delighted by these analogies, so laden with nostalgia, in the geography and epochs of disparate countries and peoples. I liked the ease with which I could now hit upon a common language with an ordinary representative of the Muslim world and how clever I was in my mentioning, during our brief encounter, the sensation of political ambivalence that pervades life under the dictatorial eastern regime whose subjects spend their lives craving Western inner freedom. In this, I said, Saddam Hussein's Baghdad was not that different from Brezhnev's Moscow.

My interlocutor eagerly seized upon my train of thought: 'Yes, yes!' he cried, 'baktyn, baktyn!' I took the word 'baktyn', with the stress on the 'a', for an affirmative Arabic interjection, something along the lines of a 'quite right!' or 'precisely, old chap!'. Developing my thought further, he said that it was precisely this mirror-like ambivalence of the East in the Russian West and the West in the Iraqi East that accounted for the popularity of 'baktyn' in translation among the Iraqi intelligentsia.

'Ahem… who?'

'Baktyn,' repeated my interlocutor. 'Mikhail Baktyn.'

I began to blush, slowly and inexorably. The realization struck that this man, whom I had taken for an Iraqi shopkeeper, was referring to Mikhail Bakhtin, legendary Russian philologist of the 1930s and creator of the philosophy of carnival and ambivalence between rulers and ruled in street art. It turned out that I was talking to Iraq's leading academic in the field of Russian philosophy and its chief translator of Mikhail Bakhtin. Like many Iraqi intellectuals, he had managed to make it to Moscow in the 1960s and on to the West, to London, in the 70s (we would have arrived at roughly the same time). He had passed through the same schooling in Russian intellectual vodka-shot chitchat as I myself had. He said my Double Z innovation had enriched his intimate knowledge of Russian culture.

A few years ago the BBC World Service had moved from Bush House to the new wing of the Broadcasting House, near Oxford Circus, as if retracing in reverse my first steps in London. But my friend from Baghdad can still enrich his intimate knowledge of Russian culture as the popularity of Double Z is spreading, even confusing my inner cartography of consuming only whisky in the west of Charing Cross Road. You can now ask for a Double Z in the Russian restaurant that was opened a couple of years ago in the heart of Soho. 'Zima' (it means simply 'Winter' in Russian) opens the doors into the enchanted world of chilled vodka shots savoured with Siberian dumplings. I'm not sure, though, whether my drink is served in the bar of the biggest bookshop in London, Waterstones, now also owned by a Russian oligarch. But some of the books on sale have Double Z in their titles - I mean my novels.

Russian publications in London used to look like samples of underground leaflets. There was a newspapers kiosk next to Holborn tube station, the nearest to Bush House, that sold international periodicals, specialising on Eastern Europe. A few years ago it had practically every daily and weekly paper published nowadays in Russia. The trade had been brisk to judge by the occasional queue of mixed origins, ages and appearances. You could easily detect amongst them a Russian customer of my 'Red émigré' generation (those who had emigrated before the collapse of the 'red'

Soviet Union): not, primarily, by his outward appearance but by the manner in which he conducted his purchase, as if it were a clandestine operation of a dirty old man buying pornography. I used to buy one of those peculiar editions to entertain Prof. Piatigorsky when I visited him at his school in the nearby Senate House. We both were amused by the vagaries of the Russian language brought about by the new wave of Russian expats in London.

One of the first serious Russian magazines twenty years ago in London was called, of course, *The Bell*, named after Herzen's historical free press. Unlike its legendary predecessor, which was printed on the cheap yellowish paper, the new *Bell* was a cross between the New Yorker and one of those thick glossy brochures that are usually put into the pocket in the back of the seat in front of you on the aeroplane. The editor of the new *Bell* was a friend of my old friend Prof. Alexander Piatigorsky. It was through this connection I got an invitation to the launch of this magazine.

At unfamiliar gatherings these days, I still tend not to disclose my Russian origin, for fear of being mistaken for an unemployed oligarch. A decade ago, at such gatherings no one bothered to introduce guests to each other, as in the good old days when it was safer to preserve anonymity in the company of potential double agents. I expected to see the old-style crowd of a few hundred Russian expatriates, the men predominantly dressed in silky black suits, but shod in cheap shoes, next to women in the dyed skins of dead animals, overloaded with swathes of jewellery. Such gatherings might have followed by a lavish reception, reminiscent of that of stuffy White Russian balls in the Café Royal in Regent Street.

And yet the Russian gathering I happened to attend, at a decorous hotel in Victoria, bore a striking similarity to any other modest business reception in London, with an air of neutrality and friendliness, the guests not showing off their wealth in the way the New Russians sometimes did. I was standing with my drink, observing the crowd of the new unusual type of Russians, when I was accosted by a friendly man who asked me whether I still think of myself as a potential victim of a near-fatal accident, and what had been my chances of survival? The question was asked in English – perhaps my interlocutor was an Englishman married to a Russian?

I pondered the question. When I emigrated from Russia to the West forty years ago, I did so voluntarily, without regarding my departure as a catastrophe, or myself as a victim of it. And yet, the idiosyncratic suggestion of the decision to emigrate as being a road accident provoked my memory into making a sentimental survey of fatal collisions in the lives of my fellow travellers in exile. As we moved with my interlocutor to fetch our drinks (Double Z again) in the bar which was outside the conference room, it was only then that I noticed the poster with the name of the gathering which I was attending: 'The Meeting of Potential Victims of Near-Fatal Accidents'.

It turned out that in this huge hotel different conventions were taking place in neighbouring conference rooms. Through another door I could see an almost identical crowd. But one figure there, dressed all in black, could not have been confused with anyone else: it was the Russian oligarch Boris Berezovsky. This time I knew I was in the right place. It did ring the correct bell. Although, having entered another room, I'd forgotten what this gathering was all about. For some of us, though, the mere presence of Berezovsky blurred the distinction between the launch of a dissident Russian magazine and the conference of potential victims of near-fatal accidents. Indeed, a decade later Berezovsky had committed suicide that some regarded as a murder.

A near fatal accident had taken place in my life for real when I went for one of my regular meeting with the same friend who had introduced me to the *Bell* magazine. Once a week we used to meet with Prof. Piatigorsky for a Chinese meal to discuss emigration as a form of religious conversion, a transgression of moral borders. An imminent philosopher and authority on Buddhism, the author of the book on Russian masons, Piatigorsky was an ardent follower of an idiosyncratic mystic Gurdjieff and he urged me not once to resist the temptation of succumbing to the life routine by choosing the most unpredictable path in life.

For one of such dates, I was waiting for him at Cambridge Circus at the crossing of Charing Cross Road and Shaftesbury Avenue. It is the Southern border of Soho so there were plenty of eccentric characters milling around the square, the location of the theatre where the musicale Jesus Christ Superstar was staged at that time. Prof. Piatigorsky, a university teacher, was usually very prompt and punctual in his appointments, but this time he had been seriously late. I was watching the motley crowd of pedestrians, looking for his tall imposing figure, dressed usually in the long black leather overcoat and the French beret. Instead, my eyes constantly met with the equally tall and imposing figure of a woman, exotically dressed in the swathes of silk and cotton of orange colours typical for Krishnaites. She had been circling around me for some time. Having waited for my Buddhist friend almost for an hour, I was hungry, and decided to go. At this moment our eyes met again and the lady in orange, without much ado, had approached me and pushed into my hands a heavy book with the garish cover. Was she a kind of messenger from Prof. Piatigorsky? I didn't have a chance to ask her as she had instantly disappeared in the crowd. I started crossing Shaftesbury Avenue with her colourful volume in my hands - an item of the clearly sectarian Krishnaite propaganda.

Shaftesbury Avenue at this point is one of those wide London streets in which a narrow strip of concrete is laid down the middle, something like a false pavement that divides the traffic into two halves. Before crossing the street, as one should in a country where they drive on the left, I naturally turned my head to the right; I reached that concrete strip in the middle and stopped there, and, waiting for the traffic to subside, had a look at the lavish edition in my hands, glamorously illustrated. On the cover, imitating the Hindu script, the illuminated title was blazing. It read, *The Direct Path to Eternity*.

I shut the book to resume my progress across the street. Before crossing the second half of the roadway, I again turned my head to the right, that is to the West. I should have, of course, looked to the opposite direction. It is hard to know why, after years in this country, I looked in the wrong direction. It may have been that as I stood on the central strip in the middle of the street, I imagined that I was standing on the pavement and was only just starting to cross the street - with its English, left-handed, traffic - and that this was why I turned my head to the right again, that is to the West, since Shaftesbury Avenue runs from west to east and I was crossing the street from the north side to the south side of it to enter Chinatown. It is also possible, however, that while standing on that false pavement and rehearsing in my memory the recent conversation about Russia, I forgot which country I was in and, imagining that I was standing in the middle of a Moscow street, I looked in the wrong direction, Soviet-fashion.

It was as if I had moved from one room to another and then was unable to remember where I had come from and decided to start from the beginning, as it were. Some psychological experiments show that the sheer act of walking through the doorway is what causes the forgetting. In my case, that doorway was the pedestrian asylum in the middle of Shaftesbury Avenue.

I even remember my astonishment at seeing the street empty, just my luck - the centre of the city, the middle of the day, and not a single car! And I stepped off. Immediately I was hit - from the left - by a motorbike. 'This is the end of my direct path to eternity,' I thought as I fell. But I was lucky: the motorcyclist managed to jam on his brakes at the last moment. For weeks on I suffered from the excruciating pain in my swollen leg, but I, a potential victim of the near fatal accident, have survived.

When I got a chance to talk to Piatigorsky, he was astounded to learn that he had let me down - so literally. He didn't remember of any planned meeting with me that day and I believed him - such a mishap had never happened before during thirty years of our friendship. We shared life not only intellectually, but geographically too, crossing the same parallels and meridians. After all, it was Piatigorsky who had lured me to move to Lewisham to become his next-door neighbour.

After seven years of suburban life, my inner compass had finally guided me back from Lewisham to Camden. It was not easy. When I, a newcomer with four years of experience of London, had moved south of the river, my British friends, with their delicate propensity not to interfere with anyone's personal decisions, did not warn me, that the moment you have crossed the river you're in another country. The effort required to move back from South London to North London is comparable to that of emigration from the Soviet Union to the West. The return to Camden was for me like a homecoming. For the last thirty years that I've been living on Haverstock Hill, I never lost my sense of orientation: I always know where my East and my West, my North and South, where to look while crossing the road. I've learnt to know where my prime meridian is.

I've also learnt that our London life is guided not along the geographical meridians and parallels, but by the routes that are defined by our friendships and fondness of certain types of places, professional interests and private obsessions.

Interestingly, a couple of years after my departure from South London, Piatigorsky also left Lewisham. He moved out of his old house, got a divorce and with his new wife settled down as my neighbour again, this time off Tavistock Place, between Euston and Russell Square. Instead of a suburban train from Lewisham to Charing Cross that we used to share, now we happened to use the same bus. 'Tavistock Place' is one of the stops on the bus route 168 which I used in order to get down south - from my house in Camden to the BBC Bush House, to Covent Garden and Soho.

It was a sheer luck that I didn't use that bus on 7th of July 2005. Not once since then I've been wondering what kind of inner cartographical links have connected the bombing of the Greenwich observatory with the act of an Islamist terrorist at Tavistock Place who could have chosen to blow up the double decker bus I might have used.

It is also worthwhile to note that it was at the distance of two bus stops up north from Piatigorsky's house on the same bus route - in the nearby Somers Town - where Joseph Conrad had chosen as the location for a pornographic cards shop and the dwelling of his double agent Verloc, an anarchist who, inspired by Bakunin's and Kropotkin's ideas, contrived in Conrad's novel to blow up the Greenwich Observatory.

At this point, I cannot resist mentioning one personal aspect of Prof. Alexander Piatigorsky's idiosyncratic appearance. He was born cross-eyed - one eye looked east, another west. He was unabashed by this inborn defect and himself joked about it when many years ago we stood for the first time together on the Prime Meridian in Greenwich.

As soon as I recollected for the second time my encounter with Prof. Piatigorsky on the Prime Meridian, it dawned on me that the memory puzzle in my mind has been completed and I have finally arrived at the beginning of a story I should have written long time ago.

Tube
Joanna Walsh

i.

In these days of national emergency, I am still waiting for love letters, into replies to which my diaries have recently been displaced.

In these days of national emergency I want not diaries but emails. It is urgent words operate outside the loop. Potential lovers become conduits for communication. The people who expect communication from me become those with whom I would like to communicate. It's a matter of approach.

London is a matter of approach. By train, on coaches. How do I know I'm there? In my parents' car, the first time, by Swiss Cottage.
Also:
Outside the Chinese laundry by which they make a racist joke, which is
(co-dependently)
prompted by the shop's own sign.

The second time was in a pale pink jacket, to be interviewed for a job I did not get. *As I was going down Saffron Hill and Saffron Hill was dirty.* I could imagine myself working in an office, something I hadn't done before, but I could not imagine what I would do there.

(This was years ago.)

In the pale pink jacket I had not worn before, I proudly took the backstreets, dirty as they were, the walls dripping as though this were some special knowledge. Though it was a job I did not get, nevertheless I was somehow eventually employed. I told the man I moved in with that I liked staying out in London after work. *Yes,* he said, *but that costs.* I did not explain my habits to him further before I moved out again.

- That the streets are a way of challenging myself.
- That I do not always enjoy it.

A woman on the London streets is still... whatever. (I can't remember now what I was going to declare: I have trouble keeping myself entirely in this world. Except for the details.)

London is language, always open to interpretation. Cards is one:

These notebooks begin after the King of Clubs or between the King of Clubs and the King of Diamonds, it must have been sometime round October last year. They also contain the following notes:

- Book recommendations from I've forgotten who: *j a baker the peregrine - sounds dreary. Vasili Rozanov - fallen leaves* (this in someone else's handwriting. Who would have recommend it?)
- In someone else's handwriting again: *Francisco Goldman Ayaozinapa WWB* (a book? An address?)
- In my handwriting: *New Yorker - The Wave. Asemic writing, AVC publications.* And
- An address,
  In someone else's writing, different again:

196A xxxxxxx Road
xxx xxx
London

I use Googlemaps. The road does not exist. Perhaps I can't read the handwriting.

From the postcode it may be an address in Waterloo.

I'd read books about London before I arrived. All the while I was reading them I was in London, and London looked exactly like the pages of a book. I had no idea how one place related to another, only the feeling of pages. I have no idea how each place relates to another, even living there.

I can always move on.

It was the feel of the pages I liked best.

ii. Cards the street dealt me: The King of Clubs.

'Wonderfully creative and very fast learners, even the careless and negative Kings of Club have keen intelligence and insight. King of Clubs are also known as emotional idealists and need to be careful they don't scatter their forces due to emotional disturbances and problems within the family.'

A woman is a vanishing act. She vanishes from one part of her life and appears in another. How she does it is up to her. When I tell men about this, the first thing they do is refuse to believe me.

[As the early system was operated by a variety of independent companies, there were no complete maps of the network. These maps were not typically schematic and were simply the line overlaid on a regular city map.]

I traced a line from the centre to where he lived. Coming to meet him, I'd go by tube although, together, we always took a cab and, by association, for a brief moment I imagined I could afford it. He said, *they pay me in cash. Sometimes I have a drawer full.* I'd come up in another life. I'd never known Stoke Newington before.

[Because it ran mostly underground, the physical locations of the stations were largely irrelevant]

In a bar on the Kingsland Road we sat on two high stools when he leaned towards me and put his middle finger into my mouth while tears streamed silently down my face. He did this for quite some time and I was not sure what to do about it but I had other things on my mind (or in my heart). I didn't see him again but walked off toward Haggerston, humming.

[The routes became more stylised but the arrangement remained, largely, geographic in nature.]

A woman in a city is what she can get away with.

A woman in the city translates, reading a space men created, in her language.

[As a schematic diagram, it does not show the geographic locations but rather the relative positions of the stations, lines, the stations' connective relations, and fare zones.]

Still I have been lucky to have encounters that facilitate communication across words and bodies,
    sex being my particular field of transgression,
    because I am not a man

    and violence is not an avenue open to me.

[The map aims to make the complicated network of services easy to understand, but it is not possible to have complete information about the services that operate on each line.]

Different men, ache stays. Ache becomes habit.

Well everyone has his own performance, and I do too. I wish there were something else I could turn to with such delight, with such delight as at the performance we produced together then and there, as if it were a trick.

[The basic design concepts have been widely adopted for other such maps around the world, and for maps of other sorts of transport networks and even conceptual schematics.]

Each man, though, prompts a style: I'm left with sentences I can write only to each. I put them in emails, address, and then delete them.

iii. Cards the street dealt me: The King of Diamonds.

'These people are willing to take a gambler's chance because they can afford to lose - but seldom do. The women King of Diamond are very positive but should strive to keep their personalities out of business dealings or they get emotionally disappointed and frustrated.'

    Ghosts are from the future. That's what I said last night. *They hammer on the windows of their past selves, can't warn them, can't get in. We don't see the ghosts. Ghosts see us only when the future touches the present.*

Dull afternoons resolve themselves into a series of objects that cannot relate. And is this quality of non-relation is what hell is? 'You make me feel comfortable,' he lied and it was almost funny.

[The map exists to help passengers navigate the rapid transit network and it has been questioned whether it should play a wider role in helping people navigate London itself.]

The man, though: what to do with him if he is still here, particularly if he has not proved satisfactory, his big body still around the place, taking up the bed, sitting at the table, demanding cups of tea, unsure even what to do with itself.

What do I want one for anyway?

(We were both most polite about it after.

Still, there is some work in trying to pretend certain encounters didn't exist. Especially if the body is still there as evidence.)

[To enable sufficient clarity of detail in the crowded central area of the map, the extremities of several lines were omitted, so a full network diagram was not provided. The problem of truncation remained for nearly half a century.]

For me hunger was part of a going forth--sex also--for him, a reward at the end of things: he always knew when he'd had enough. With him I felt greedy. He came politely like someone placing his cutlery together at the side of his plate after a meal, and I knew then that he could not be generous, sexually, that--by limiting them--he kept his pleasures quietly to himself. Also his cunnilingus was no more than cursory: *box* ticked.

[Dashed lines have at various times indicated routes with limited service, lines under construction or lines closed for renovation]

But he was a real text-addict (I don't mean txt like on a phone). He always wanted more--in that way at least. As for me all I want is to keep talking.

As if I could fill any kind of gap with words.

[Because the map ignores geography, it does not accurately depict the relative orientation and distance between stations. Those traveling from Bank Station to Mansion House would, based on the map, take the Central Line to Liverpool Street, change to the Circle Line, travel five more stops, and arrive at a station that is 200 feet away from the start of the trip.]

The one thing he did that I liked was stroke my hair. I miss tenderness, but I have suffered such a good deal from it, or rather from the things that have been expected of me in exchange, that I have become suspicious, and decided to need it less often. Last night I stayed with friends in Walthamstow. When their TV goes on standby the screen becomes a family photo album and images scroll by— of them standing together: on the beach, in a field, with relatives, at places designed to facilitate days out, at parties. I don't have photos like this. Walking through the Lloyd Park this morning, I saw mothers engaged in the disgusting business of *bringing up* their children, a phrase that also means vomiting.

iv. Cards the street dealt me: the ten of diamonds

'The Ten of Diamond is the most important of the money Cards, and not surprisingly, placed in the exact centre of the Life Spread of Cards. Man chose to make money the pivotal point around which all life revolves, and the 10 of Diamond is considered the most powerful of the money cards in order to symbolize its success.'

In the back of the notebook is the number I never called when going to see him.

(That greed for that final email, that will never come.

Because someone has to stop.

Because I have used it already.)

[In some cases, stations within short walking distance are now shown, often with the distance between them.]

I looked at a photo of him online this morning, not of him. It moved me more to see him in the background, unaware, of a London pub. I misread its sign: The Compleat Tangler. I am a camera, which is in turn a duct for words. I am now almost entirely words with hardly the time to be where I describe. I pretended to a friend that I had seen this photo by chance: in fact I searched for it, knowing he was there, hoping-not-hoping I would see him.

This morning the photo caused me no anxiety; yesterday it hurt me very much. But yesterday I was tired.

[Some commentators have suggested it should be replaced with a new design that can incorporate new lines more comfortably]

I went there, walked there: *Doors where my heart...* La Scala's tooth-gapped stage. Somers Town: boys playing in the street, a Doisneau photo, but they're Albanian. Where was our place for it? In Saint Martin's Gardens? How could that intersect with history? We witnessed the monuments there, being the only ones that stayed still long enough.

[Attempts to create alternative versions to the official map have continued.]

Nowhere to go now on the London streets; nowhere to go but indoors. London's an inside city, but as soon as you think you're in, it puts you outside like a revolving door. Never a city with so much exterior: the cold, the rain gets under my skin, into my bones. Above the tube's entrance, octagonal panopticons faceted for maximum surface. There must be some 'ins' to these 'outs', but I've never seen them. Those tables and chairs outside the cafes are not fooling anyone. The only ones that work are on the station, vaulted over by iron and glass: the outside turned in.

...and think of early days and thee.

They will soon not matter, these beautiful interiors. They will have no value. The number of homeless men in the streets is increasing. I'd wanted to walk them with someone I'd walked them with before, someone who gave me permission to break everything.

(He was, himself, quite conservative.)

He said *I keep moving. If I keep moving it doesn't seem so bad.*

What I wrote but did not send: *No, I'm not your friend. When I see you, I want to put my hands on your body. That's not the same as friendly. I want to put your dick in my mouth; I want you to fuck me every way you know how. I want to curl around you afterwards and sleep with you all night.*

It could have applied to any of them and, as it is, I have had enough of them, more than I can count on my fingers and my toes. I don't have room in my heart or my brain for any more. So now I'm leaving.

And the tour guide in the street says, 'guys guys guys guys guys guys guys guys guys guys.'

v. Cards the Street Dealt Me: the 7 of clubs

'The Seven of Clubs challenge rests in the negative aspects of the mind, which are worry, doubt and pessimism. Today you have the opportunity to maintain positive, healthy thoughts. Any contact with spiritual thoughts or ideals is sure to have a positive effect and help offset any negative thinking.'

'Don't do things you'll be ashamed of,' becomes, *'Don't be ashamed of the things you do.'*

Whatever they are, they will become you, like the streets. To accept them, all it takes is a small effort of will.

About my feet.

On every street I've hoped to see a face, as none belong to me alone.

Having sympathy for all limping people, I see one, distressed to be caught in her own body. I know what it's like to hobble. What I'm interested in is the coping mechanism, how things in general become a management of aching. In my special case I still expect this not to continue.

In the meantime, there are all the pretty boys at parties who like me until they think to ask, *how old are you?* (I answer random numbers). There is, of course, beforehand, a moment of hope, that moment I allow myself to believe I am about to be given something I didn't even know I wanted, for free.

Not used to being limited in my movements,
I have thought a lot about 'self-limiting' conditions.

Like the man who kissed me at the party. It was at that very point I discovered I was not a free woman, with all the limitations of freedom. A Chinese sword hung over his bed, and when he said something that frightened me very much, that neither of us could remember after, but it was one of those sentences that reminded me that sometimes men visit violence on women, and that he might be one of those men, I put on my clothes and told him I was leaving, though I did not leave.

I am limited by the condition of my foot, but even that has its limits.

For the moment, though, so do I.

And so it is I find my myself early in the morning at a station cafe--in despite of having lost my taste for eating alone in public--congratulating myself on not having sustained too much damage of any kind. And even this is not original: the narrative I live is not one I made for myself, as none of ours are. However, retold, it's unusual enough to draw hostility, even from close friends. It's hard to be told so often I'm not living right. Well, enough of this Rhysing around. Perhaps...

I find my condition is called plantar fasciitis.
I identify it only after I am able to imagine it as a condition.
Before it was only pain

There are things I must not want, that I find that perhaps, after all, I do not want.

I identified my condition after my foot stopped hurting.
I noticed this only a while after because
It was a lack of noticing.

I noticed all this while I was sitting in the cafe, at which point I was able to get up quite easily, and walk away. It was here in London I learned to walk away. With pleasure.

Or--no--I trained myself. In fact

all this I had done in preparation for walking away. And look at me now: a woman who can afford her own toast--and moral predicaments! Because I paid for it, I will eat every little bit. Sometimes I am hungry for more words; sometimes I worry words are fed me too easily. I have been told I tie them too close to flesh. Too close for whom?

> *I begin to question how much, at crucial moments*
> *I ever felt it,*
> *I have blanked it from my memory.*
> *It's always the pain I forget.*

My phone still autocorrects words to men's names, and I do not like to turn the heating up to 'Max'.

vi: no card

Finally it got cold. The streets transacted. There are now homeless people here who smile, who display themselves in families, who read their phones, who play with their children. It is possible now to be homeless in any way.

Theirs are stories no one wants to hear, that are not written. There are stories you must pretend do not exist, if you want to get by. Especially in a city. You see them on every street corner. These are not even remarkable stories.

All the people in whose arms I have imagined myself folded this year to sleep--and some I really have: G like a carved saint most aptly... then all the others. I can fold myself now into my imagining of them. It is almost corporeal. This year a man put my hand on his dick and told me that was what I should call home. Instead, I gave money to a beggar setting out his pitch-- a small neat stack of personal items beside a closed shop--because he applied aftershave from a bottle.

Resistance is something done in life, not writing.

To write against what you feel is a literary situation. In other words: to lie.

Having approached each new man like an edifice, increasingly wary of what might be inside, I have registered my habit of thinking they are utopias (the future also, and cities), but it is one thing to fight each instance, another the structures that support them.

Any kind of pain is a matter of time.

*

At a certain age it stops being unnecessary that shoes are not uncomfortable. Then, at a certain age it becomes necessary that they are comfortable. But sometimes, even so, you will fall over on the street and there will be no one waiting at home. When I did, it was on the pavement late at night. I made small scream, which was an afterthought that justified the action. My worry was, the man who helped me up would think I that was drunk, and I was not drunk. I scrutinised the man's face for the recognition he was helping an old lady. It was the first time I'd ever thought to do that.

Before, I'd slipped a few times, but slipping made me feel I'd never fall

because each time I rescued myself.

Sometimes I can't even see the bruises after.

But one day it will hurt.

It is lonely to fall and have no one to tell.

It is lonely to fall and to worry you might be hurt and have no one to ask for help.

It is lonely to know that one day this will happen again, and another time. And then for the last time.

When I took off my shoes to go to bed I found the shape of my feet had changed. I had not examined them for a long time. They seemed longer, narrower, and softer than they were. This had not happened before.

vii: no card

What was London? It was language! I had already modified my words to fit those I read, mostly around tube stations, on dirty kiosks, their signs in every--as though, by repeating a word, it could be, somewhere else, invoked! For instance, people started saying the word 'apocalypse' for fun around Eastertime. We won't recognise it when it arrives. I, for one, will still be typing. Even about fear.

We are a stupid nation, we have sold
- Weekends to weekdays.
- Foreignness to ourselves.
- Triviality to the upper classes.

We don't understand why our children no longer have these things. They'd seemed to come to us free and without limit. But, suddenly, there are too many disasters for history. Even my ex begins to refer to himself as 'working class' out loud.

Because sides are being chosen.

And now I'm leaving.

I had already left. Why did I ever expect a welcome? The city is moving inside me. When I get up from my chair in any bar now, I no longer know how many suitcases I have with me. I have applied for a postal vote forever, and I don't turn cards up in the street any more.

There are women who ride the tube with their eyes open.
There women who ride the tube with their eyes shut.
I still have not decided which I am.

Sadly--though I can never live here--this is my capital.

Notes:

Material in *[parentheses]* adapted from:
https://en.wikipedia.org/wiki/London_Underground

Card readings from:
https://thecardsoflife.com/
and https://www.metasymbology.com/

London, an exercise in learning
Susana Moreira Marques

Lessons

I

I live on the 5th floor of a modernist 1950's building in East London. It's a small flat but because it has a large window with a view of the city it feels bigger. To the west, I see a bit of the London Eye. To the southeast, there's Canary Wharf with its high rises. Closer by, the high rises of the City. In between, rows of typical English houses. Here and there, spots of green.

As far as my eye can see, it's London. I can spend a long time contemplating the city. I love it particularly at dusk, when the lights are suddenly turned on and soon sparkle the darkness.

In that view labour millions of lives. Yet, the feeling is akin to contemplating the desert: if I'd like - or even if I wouldn't - I could disappear without a trace. I am a dot of light in a complex firmament that goes largely unstudied.

If I wake up at night, I come to the living-room, stand by the window, and study the map created by the lights in the dark. I think of the lives I could have lived. That, perhaps, I still can.

II

It's in London that I start the habit not only of observing attentively passers-by in the streets, but also of taking notes about them. I have always carried a notebook with me but before I mainly used it to take notes about myself.

There's always something inspiring to notice walking in London: a small act of love or hate. It can be an uplifting sight: a child playing; two lovers in the park; a person dressed as if she was from another time. Or it can be disturbing and sad: a pretty woman begging in the street; a loud argument during a bus ride; the fear in someone who avoids eye contact; an old man not fitting the scenery, looking like he's waiting to be taken away.

I know that I'll probably never use these notes. Or, at least, not the large majority of them. I'm aware that this is more like drawing a landscape - filling a space with shapes, colours and details - than writing a narrative. I have no stories for these people. It would feel like a betrayal to imagine stories for them, for they have come here with their all too real stories, and it takes them a lot of effort just to be themselves.

Nevertheless, I keep this habit. I take notes. I dutifully fill in the blank pages.

III

A homeless man died at the doors of the Houses of   Parliament. He was found dead one morning after a particularly cold night. A friend of the homeless man found dead at the doors of the   Houses of Parliament told the press that he didn't understand it, as if death was understandable. The friend of the homeless man, who was also homeless, said he had seen him just the day before and that he looked well and strong, this meaning not only that he looked in good health but also that he seemed willing to go on living. He had been going regularly to a shelter, the friend added. The press said that Members of Parliament, who remembered the homeless man, since he had been living rough in the area for some time, posted their condolences. They wrote nice words to be shared online. They spoke about their responsibility towards *all* people, or, *the* people.

The reports added that the man was forty   and Portuguese, minor details in a story that spoke at large about poverty and indifference, a story that seemed to perfectly summarise the cruelty of life in a large city and that, since he had died so close to the centre of power, provided a good metaphor for a world where words and actions are often at odds.

His story was familiar, one of those narratives that have always been told and will keep being told. It was the reverse of the success story and it served as warning: a young man, full of life and ambition, comes to the big city to make it; he works in cafes to pay for his living while he dreams of   his dream job; he then loses his job at the cafe and the following jobs; he sleeps in friend's flats; he sleeps rough; he lives in the street; he's dead.

Reading the newspapers, we do not learn the details of how he took the wrong turn, if it happened suddenly or gradually, since that doesn't matter for purposes of a cautionary tale: only the outcome matters. We also don't learn much about his background. We don't know if he had a happy childhood and youth, or why he decided to move to London. We don't know if the man who was found dead at the doors of the Houses of Parliament had an old girlfriend or boyfriend who would think fondly of him and mourn him. Nor do we know if his mother was still alive, speaking - in the moment the press was writing - the unspeakable.

The fact that he was forty, like me, and that he was Portuguese, like me, makes it easier for me to think that that man could have been me or - changing the verb to a more accurate tense - can be me.

Politicians talked about *all* people or *the* people; they never said he was *their* people. Can I say he's *my* people?

IV

At the local library, a man approaches me and asks me to marry him. He's from Bangladesh. He says his name. He says he noticed I wasn't wearing a ring on my finger. He looks serious and respectful, in an old fashioned way. He dresses plainly in dark clothes. He has a handsome smile. I can't say if he's older than me or if he's a very young man who looks old.

I'm not upset neither am I flattered by the approach. I'm entertained. Maybe I am grateful for that bit of attention. I think of the effort necessary in taking those few steps to reach me in the library: across a division between communities that we've become accustomed to. In that moment we are rather the neighbours we ought to be. We have a common language, an adopted language, and we use it. We are a man and a woman, we are descendants of other men and women, with their centuries of understandings and misunderstandings.

I reply as if this was a common request: I explain that I have a boyfriend; *I'm to be married soon,* I lie; I look at my hand, as if there is an imaginary ring on my finger, and I smile.

V

Go to the nearest busy street and watch people go by. Choose a face or two in the crowd. People are usually unguarded when walking on a London busy street, because they are so focused in getting from A to B, in starting their day or finishing their day, in surviving the routine.

At the beginning, I do it all the time. I marvel at the variety of people: the world on show. At first, I see mainly people's differences and only after a while, I start to see sameness in their features. Then, gradually, I turn into one of the people I watch. Me, with my clothes; me, with my way of walking; me, with my accent; me, with my colour of skin; me, with my colour of hair; me, with my way of catching my hair; me, with my backpack; me, with my shoes; me, with my absorbed expressions; me, getting from A to B; me, surviving the routine; me, unguarded: me, a face in the crowd.

VI

Every day I leave the house to get coffee and to have to come back home, so I start working with a sense of purpose.

One morning I buy flowers. I buy flowers because they're there and they're pretty. I don't even buy them at a flower shop. I buy them at the supermarket with half pint of milk and bread.

Roses. Roses are roses are roses. White ones.

I don't feel at all like a Mrs. Dalloway, starting a day that can shed light into all my life. I'm not sure I'd want to find a thread linking my choices, leading me to this day. There needs not to be a connection to what was before and what comes after. Perhaps, that's the great thing about changing one's geography.

I buy flowers because they're there and they're pretty and I've decided I want to have more pretty things in my life. It's simple. It's not symbolic. It's not revealing. Nor is it meaningful that the flowers will wither and die in three days.

At home I put the flowers in a jug that doubles as a vase. I put the vase in the dining table that doubles as my working table. I sit and open my laptop to start working.

Yes, they are pretty, the roses, for their price.

VII

I've already used this image in a text once: flowers growing where bombs hit during the Blitz - renewal after destruction; life after death.

It's a hopeful image. It perfectly captures the essence of the world - and our world, still - that it resists elaboration. It's a quiet image, very still. There's a silence to it, even a deafness, like the deafness after the blast. It's also a textured image, with hard materials in ruins, the crumbling soft material of dust and earth - and the flowers. It's an image without standing grand buildings and without any people.

I look at the picture often, I see it again in my head, I use it as a favourite for several purposes, but mainly to not lose sight of the thought that we'll be replaced. If we're lucky, by flowers.

VIII

His hands are beautiful, with long fingers. Though strong they look delicate. He touches the fruit in the tree that bends over someone else's wall, and that's when I notice that his nails are dark with dirt. We have been talking for a couple of hours about trees, edible leaves and fruits. He's a city boy but he knows the names of trees, plants, flowers. This is not unusual in London, where there seems to be a need to take care of plants. I suspect that there's a sense of ownership in the gesture - and of belonging. It's such an old concept, and an infallible one: if you have a bit of land to grow things, then the land is yours; even if just for one season to see a tree bear fruit.

As he tells me about his life, I observe his hands, his face, his body. His hands and face and body tell me that his tale is true. He was born into a world of privilege and while he still lingers in that world, with its rules, its confidence, its accent, he's breaking away from it. He doesn't tend a garden. He makes a garden of the whole of London. He roams the public parks for food and takes pleasure in stealing from private ones. He tells me that there are entire squares filled with trees that are privately owned.

He has a beard, thick like that of a man living away in the woods, but I can see that he still trims it. He has stopped buying food and he only eats what he finds. This might seem like the past but, of course, he does it believing it's the future. He is the man of the future; a template. He gets himself dirty but then he washes up and writes in his Apple computer about how to live without going to a supermarket. He researches on how to find food or on how to kill an animal and skin it, and other lost primal instincts and skills. He has a studied smile, polite and seductive, but I notice that some of his teeth are going black, so I believe it when he tells me that at dawn he hunts for animals in the outskirts of London and eats them. He has become quiet good at it, he adds.

IX

And how I study. I buy the newspaper everyday, with a kind of religious devotion. I turn the habit into discipline: I get my fingers dirty with newspaper ink in the belief that information is still useful.

Every day I yearn to find out how much I still can't read or understand. I look in the dictionary for the meaning of words but there are whole sentences and paragraphs, there are statements, quotations, arguments, suggestions, allusions, critiques, jokes, there are so many images that I still can't read; there is so much to decipher that the challenge will never be completed.

It's not like learning a new language, but to speak again.

X

At first, I love the brick. Then, I start to resent its repetitiveness: every life played against the same backdrop.

Look at that elderly black man. He wears an old suit. He's old fashioned. He wears a hat. He walks elegantly, in a slow pace, as if trying to be in control of every one of his movements. Yet, for all his efforts, he becomes invisible. He seems to dissolve against the backdrop of his neighbourhood. He walks but he's going nowhere. I can't know what's in his mind: if he thinks of his childhood, if he longs for the sights, sounds and smells of a distant home, or not at all.

Perhaps he feels like he has no choice but to roam these streets. He knows only too well that life cannot be undone, nor would he want to: kids and grandkids, rents and jobs and bank accounts, and friends, alive and dead, and small everyday habits. The years have run by quicker than expected.

He walks the streets, knowing that he's walking in circles. He might recognise in his neighbours that same look of being locked up, though with plenty of fresh air and eventually the happiness of sharing the time with people they love.

XI

I must be four or five. Perhaps my mother is already pregnant with my sister. My father, who rarely travels, has gone on a business trip and has just arrived from London. I'm excited to see him again. He brings a present from that faraway place. I unwrap it. It's a crib for my baby doll. It's red with tiny white flowers.

The memory of us three in our living-room, in that moment, is quite precise amongst the amalgam of vague and drifty images that form my childhood. I'm not sure why I remember this so well or even if there's at all a reason for some memories to endure and others to be lost.

Like everyone, I guess I'd like to believe some things in life are meant to be, rather than randomly happening; no cause, no effect: no narrative. Like everyone, contrary to reasonable expectations, I've been looking for the person I'm meant to be with, the work I'm meant to do, and the place I'm meant to live in.

To Do's

To learn invisibility. To strive for it. To blossom in it, because no one is looking. To learn to spend days nameless. To learn anonymity to the point you'll know exactly why you no longer wish to remain anonymous, unknown, unaccounted for.

To learn to talk about the weather. Because if we might know the words for so many things they might correspond to different images to different people and the weather is there: a sky above; grey, wet, cloudy, clear, blue, bright. To learn to speak by increments, each time revealing a bit more.

To learn to make a fool of yourself, since you've come this far anyway. To learn to be disdained for your foolishness or admired for it, since it can so often mean that you are daring.

To learn to play it all, win it all, lose it all. To learn to expect the opportunity to play it all, win it all, lose it all.

To learn to be patient. To learn to wait for your turn, because so many people are waiting for their turn - at a bus stop, at a line in the post office, at a job, at an opportunity, at a break, at a dream, at happiness - why should you go first? To learn kindness in the face of distress. To learn how to show that kindness, through small gestures. To learn to say things with the eyes to comfort strangers you are not advised to talk to. To learn to use politeness as a useful tool.

To learn to measure the excitement, the overwhelming excitement that comes with newness. To learn to quantify the experience and describe it with joy but without losing sobriety. To learn to keep a record if only in your memory.

To learn to keep it real in a scenery that's too often part of fictional narratives, or historical narratives so far fetched that they might as well be fictional. To learn to resist the temptation of following the parallel story, the unlived story, the what-ifs of life.

To learn to love a neighbourhood or just a street or even just a bit of a street like people love a small town or a village. To learn to love protectively, defensively, and always fiercely as if your honour depended on it. To learn to love old-fashionably, to say I will commit to love this neighbourhood, this street or even this tiny bit of street for as long as I may live here, no matter how little time in this fast-moving world.

To learn to believe in place as knowledge. To learn to continuously believe knowledge can save.

To learn to hope. To learn to say: perhaps today wasn't a good day, but tomorrow will be.

The Loveless House

Vanni Bianconi

Staircases,

The social condensers of Berthold Lubetkin

Berthold Lubetkin was a ferro-concrete engineer and architect. Born in present-day Georgia at the turn of the twentieth century, he studied in Moscow and Leningrad, moved to Paris then to London in 1931. Among the most distinctive features of his architecture are the staircases he places at the structural core of social housing tower blocks. They are there to have an impact on lives, fine and failed examples of *social condenser*, a spatial idea that has been defined as 'programmatic layering upon vacant terrain to encourage dynamic coexistence of activities and to generate through their interference unprecedented events.' Unprecedented events.

Lubetkin's penguin pool ramps are a social condenser, and so is his Finsbury Health Centre: 'the Centre's opening arms and entrance were a deliberate attempt to introduce a smile into what is a machine,' said Lubetkin of his seminal building. Settled down on vacant terrain amid the grey-brown slums of Finsbury, this 'strange new bird of brilliant plumage' had a body of reinforced concrete and wings consisting of hollow tile floors supported by perimeter beams and structural mullions, partially clad with faience tiles and thermolux glass panels, 'as beautiful as the hair of a beautiful young girl in the summer sunshine.'

Not far from it, in 1902-03, lived Lenin. In 1942 Lubetkin convinced Finsbury Council to erect a Lenin memorial on that very terrain, made vacant by intense enemy bombing, and later to build a large estate that was to be named Lenin Court. But unprecedented events occurred and, by the time

the building was completed, WWII allies had become Cold
war enemies, so that its name was changed from Lenin to
Bevin, a post-war anti-communist foreign secretary. As for
the memorial, it was repeatedly defaced, and contested in
Parliament, until the day Lubetkin interfered: he rented a
crane, removed the monument and buried it at the rear of
the estate's building site, where there is now a car park.
Some say. Others say that the memorial was buried in a
basement of the building. But most say that it is buried at
the bottom of its staircase. A radial stair in a circular well.

I first noticed and got to know Lubetkin's architecture,
and with it a few features of my immediate environment,
because of one such staircase.

My ground floor apartment is located at the rear of an
east London new-build, one of those featuring no façade
but only a rear on each side. One of the main architectural
events here, the Great Fire, occurred in 1666; due to the
quick urbanisation of the Victorian era, large parts of town
were built in the 1860's; and in the 1960's the post-war tower
blocks changed the city's skyline. The number six must play a
role in London architecture, and it's in 2016 that asymmetric
new-builds have simultaneously appeared everywhere
around town. I live in one of them and everywhere I spot
my kind of house, housing my kind of life. With the one
difference that my ground floor apartment shows unusually
large windows all along its external perimeter. The view
from one of the windows is mostly occupied by a large
Y-shaped tower block, that warms my heart when is lit up
at night, dries it when it's dark in the daytime, and is called
the Loveless House.

Ground floor,

No spitting

Some of the people living in the estate are sensitive to the permeability of my apartment, a factor strange to London living, and feel encouraged to knock on the safety glass, to shout something or to run off. Some stay for a chat. One of them wanted to show me something in his building, it had to do with the decorative oval at the centre-top of its façades. In contrast to my type of building, the Loveless House (this is indeed its name) is only composed of façades, one for each of its concave, open-armed elevations, made dynamic by the coexistence of its pre-fab components. My neighbour had not come by to talk about the oval moulding, the one at the top the Loveless façade, but we started chatting and I must have said, 'The saints up there,' pointing upwards. He had a shy smile that lingered, directed to no one in particular. That half smile, I discovered, could suddenly disappear, then a rage in his eyes seemed aimed at everyone and everything at once, and so was his swearing.

'What saints, what arse-fucking saints?' was his reply. I insisted they were clearly two saints, even if just to keep on chatting, and we ended up betting 20 quid on that.

'What's your name, lad?' I asked.

'Garret, mate.'

'And you live in that building?'

'That's where I live. Loveless, born and bred,' he said, and half-smiled to the building.

'Well, Gary, let's do it!' I locked all my windows, then my door, and followed Gary towards the estate, which I was about to enter for the first time.

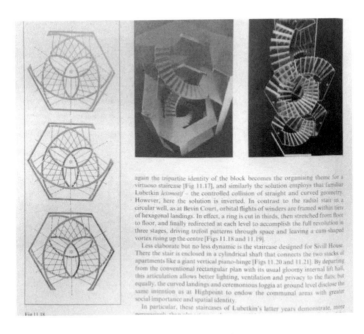

again the tripartite identity of the block becomes the organising theme for a virtuoso staircase [Fig 11.17], and similarly the solution employs that familiar Lubetkin *leitmotif* – the controlled collision of straight and curved geometry. However, here the solution is inverted. In contrast to the radial stair in a circular well, as at Bevin Court, orbital flights of winders are framed within tiers of hexagonal landings. In effect, a ring is cut in thirds, then stretched from floor to floor, and finally redirected at each level to accomplish the full revolution in three stages, driving trefoil patterns through space and leaving a cam-shaped vortex rising up the centre [Figs 11.18 and 11.19].

Less elaborate but no less dynamic is the staircase designed for Sivill House. There the stair is enclosed in a cylindrical shaft that connects the two stacks of apartments like a giant vertical piano-hinge [Figs 11.20 and 11.21]. By departing from the conventional rectangular plan with its usual gloomy internal lift hall, this articulation allows better lighting, ventilation and privacy to the flats; but equally, the curved landings and ceremonious loggia at ground level disclose the same intention as at Highpoint to endow the communal areas with greater social importance and spatial identity.

In particular, these staircases of Lubetkin's latter years demonstrate, more

Fig 11.18

The staircase, the staircase, that Lubetkin staircase…

Every time I read this sentence its rhythm prompts me to pronounce the repeated word in two ways: correctly, stressing the *stair* half of it, the first two times; incorrectly, I guess, because of the anapaestic pace of the second hemistich, stressing the *case* part of it, the third time. This is comparable to the effect the staircase had on me. Since we went through the main door and I found myself staring at its staircase, the towering block is the same and it isn't.

We wouldn't have taken the stairs if the elevator had been working that day. Gary swore and spat, despite the 'No spitting' sign in English and Bengali. When I pointed at the staircase and argued it was beautiful, he didn't hear me. 'Fuck the fucking stairs,' I remember him saying.

First floor,

The difficulties of truth amidst desperate evil

The steps have an ideal height, it's very easy to tread upon them gathering momentum, as well as to keep a steady and more relaxed pace. One can also pick the ideal depth climbing more toward the centre or more toward the banister, because of the helical structure of the staircase. Helical, but here with a tripartite radius, which employs a familiar Lubetkin leitmotif: the controlled collision of straight and curved geometry. Orbital flights of winders are framed within tiers of hexagonal landings. In effect, a ring is cut into thirds, then stretched from floor to floor, and finally redirected at each level to accomplish the full revolution in three stages, driving threefold patterns through space and leaving a cam-shaped vortex rising up the centre.

Being a cochlear labyrinth of revolving ducts, and oval too, like the oval window in our ears, this seemingly sensorial structure deploys its own cilia as well: the lean black posts of the banister, climbing concentrically from bottom to top. Through them, while I am still moving elliptically away from the first floor's landing, I see a swollen arm that someone shows to someone else.

'What the fuck,' goes the someone else.

'Two days I have been back man, two days!' says the arm.

'And it got all swollen again mate?'

'Yeah, bloody luck, innit. I go back, to prove them, that they did good to keep me, you know, they didn't have to, but I do my job, yeah, and when I'm in that kitchen they know it – the young ones, the ones who like to take a rest here and there, when I'm in it no they don't rest shit you know, I'm on their case, I'm there to tell them: 'Done your job yet? Washed them pots over there?'

'Yeah…'

'Sure they kept me, even if six weeks out of the job, I was a bit afraid you know, can't afford to lose me job again, mate, well not really afraid, a little you know. When it happened last they told me 'You mad, go to the hospital man, what are you doing here?' – you know, good people, my boss, they like me, innit. But now I go in, for two days, two fucking days mate, and the boss sees me arm all swollen again, he sees. He tells me 'Go to the GP right now, be back soon,' he tells me, 'be back soon,' he tells me –'

Second floor,

The possibility that love is not enough

We couldn't, or at least I couldn't, help slowing down and hearing them talk, the two neighbours on the landing, all the way up to the second floor and almost further when the singing started up:

> *Same old rascal-al, takin' the piissss*
> *Same old rascal-al, takin' the piissss*
> *Same old rascal-al, takin' the piissss*

Third floor,

Honour this and that

And then a whispering from upstairs made us, or made me, climb more alertly. Two voices, an elderly woman's and an elderly man's.

'In my letterbox: I found it there,' she says.

'Found what' that's him.

'Found this: *Your voice as if silence repented*' she reads.

'What does it even mean.'

'It's the letter, the letter *he*, the other one, had sent me. And *you* had it. Here: *Your hair like harvest wheat*. You found it, ten years back, and you – and I moved out of this damphole of yours. I had to move in with that Flat 14 lady, didn't I, horrible that was. I nearly jumped off a window back then. Not that you would remember. Now you know it, what bloody letter?'

'I do not know it, because I didn't put anything in your letterbox. But you threatening of jumping from a first floor, I remember that, alright.'

'Moving your horrible cupboard, right there, that's how you found his letter, when *he*, the letter guy, had long moved out of the building altogether, and yet you decided that we, that I –'

'Deeds alone decide for deeds to come –'

Fourth floor,

An accent that has been described variously as Scandinavian, American or Scottish

My eavesdropping interrupted by singing, again, this time, though, seemingly coming from the elevator, from inside the broken elevator. That would mean that someone is locked inside and is singing. Then the same voice, the elevator's, so to speak, stops singing, starts talking, to me, or so it seems, the way I'm seemingly talking to you.

*How formidable, to hear what was just said, voices alright, and
as such almost deprived of body, and yet so much more palpable,
in their fear, of losing a job, in the remains of a life-time romance
reduced to door-numbers and floors. Intimate, vulnerable, in ways
people seldom are. And why is that?*

An accelerated speech-flow on my right-hand side. One
kid explaining something to another with such drive it grabs
my attention and I leave the elevator's question unanswered,
despite the language barrier growing even higher now:

'আর বল তো – ও type কীকরে করে? অপেক্ষা করে – যে
অক্ষরটা চায় – cursor সেখানে পৌঁছয় – অমনি গালের muscleটা
নাড়ায়।'

'এই Stephen Hawking কি গালের muscle ছাড়া আর কিছু
নাড়াতে পারে না?'

'ধুর বোকা! তা না হলে কি কেউ গাল দিয়ে লেখে? muscle টা নাড়ায়
– signal টা পাঠায় – cursor টুক করে অক্ষরটা ধরে নেয় আর আবার
চলতে শুরু করে – পরের অক্ষরটার দিকে – আবার গাল দেওয়া – আবার
টুক করে click করা।'

'গাল দেওয়ার এক্কেবারে নতুন মানে বার করলি, মামা!'

'You're such an idiot!'

The kids switch to English once we are up the next flight
of stairs, and this makes me listen in even harder, but what
I pick up comes from the elevator's side, is uttered in a soft
voice, if quite robotic, that I've heard before:

*Knowing how laborious the whole operation is makes you
appreciate more whatever he might write, as if the writing process
itself may benefit from being infused with deep boredom and a
suffering that is mostly procedural.*

Staircase,

Canon

The low metallic voice coming from my left side seemed to respond to the voices on my right – even if I couldn't be sure. There Gary, who didn't seem to be hearing any of this, or anything at all, stopped, sat down on the steps, looked me in the eye, maybe for the first time, and spoke.

'Social media's logorrheic nonsense, the social-me's, the fake-you's. Fucking hate it. But I have my own plan. Didn't quite find the name yet, Deadbook, Face-off or something, there one has a limited, and I mean limited, set of posts. A hundred in total, say, then you're done, it don't matter if someone answers you or writes about you.' He got up, restarted walking, but kept talking, lowering his voice now. 'Like my sister, fucking unbelievable, that's all she cares about. So she'll learn to be careful about what she writes and it'll mean something, for those who read her. Like the wishes, you know, the magic spells one got for a haunted wood, they were always numbered, they were.'

Now definitely coming from the elevator, a loud sound, like *Beeeoooonnnnggggggggggg,* like music, interrupts Gary's ramble. Face-off… now that he's finally talking to me, what the hell is he going on about? The same sound again, possibly the elevator ropes, plucked by a giant hand. Then again, the low, articulate voice, not Gary's, the elevator's.

Not artificial intelligence, I wouldn't call it that, rather we progress towards algorithmically enhanced human idiocy. The relation with the machine is contagious: the machine facilitates automations, that's what it does, and if a simple lift prevents you from being exposed to your neighbours' noises and quarrels, pleasures and worries, imagine what is occurring now that the so called A.I. plays a role in most physical and mental processes and assists you in deciding both your sleeping patterns and your sleeping partners –

Fifth floor,

Saturday night and Saturday morning

'Madam, let me ask you again, kindly. I had a long day and the day has barely started. For most people, that is. I've been up since five o' clock this morning.'

'Five? Listen, *sir*, I got up at four thirty myself, but I don't go around whining about it, nor is it a reason for me to go touch other folks' property.'

'Lift's broken. I had to climb all the way up, and the bright woman you are, you can easily tell I'm past the flower of youth. If I was leaning on your window-sill, it was only to catch my breath. I have no interest whatsoever in such trinkets, madam, I swear: not in Bevin the dwarf, here, nor in the pretty mermaid there…'

'What I can easily tell you is that I know your type: were we hit by a natural catastrophe such as a broken lift, God forbid, you're the type that'd sooner take shelter in the pub, no matter how early it is, rather than finally do himself some good by walking up a few steps, as I do, every day, twice, at least.'

'I can testify that the elevator is actually down, madam, and that the gentleman here was climbing the stairs, and with audible effort, just a few moments ago.'

Indeed – and this is me writing to you, and in the previous sentence it was me talking to them – I had heard him panting up the stairs a few moments before. This turned out to be irrelevant: the neighbours looked at each other and after a pause, a short and meaningful one, they carried on with their row as if I hadn't spoken at all. Except for a passing reference to 'morons like that one' and, possibly, the outburst of laughter as soon as I turned my back. By then Gary was addressing me, with a sly smile now, and like he had known me for more than a few minutes, and I was even listening to him.

'You Christian cunts. You don't know what to do with all that charity gushing out of you.'

'Oh shut up Gary. I'm not even baptised. Hey: they seem to enjoy their quarrel, those two, don't you think, tailoring insults for one another. You know, in my town –'

'Zombie Christianism, or whatever you choose to call it, but that's what you're made of. Two-dimensional pity. You tear your little pity square, stimulate your salivary glands and lick it and stick it on the less fortunate ones, ready to be well-wishingly sent off to your postcard awakening. That's exactly why you can be so blinded to see saints up in our oval.'

'Now you know you lost the bet when you start rambling about mercy…'

I leaned on the bannister for a moment, I looked all the way down, then up. I'd done nothing wrong, on both occasions, if you ask me, but something was off – something escaped me. Then like a blast someone ran through us, as it were, ran past us and we stood there without really knowing what we saw or heard

Staircase,

Nolite timere

because she ran down so fast, and almost noiselessly – her steps pacing downwards were just a soft crescendo that rose and whirled until she sped past between us like a wind and when she was gone her sound was faint and fading – if almost, it seemed, dangerous. For some time we – this time I'm sure that Gary was listening in too – were expecting a second set of sounds from the floors above, people shouting in a rage or some brutal movement. There are events that rhyme, one first boot thrown on the floor, a car braking and the crash. Now the footsteps lapsed their rhyme – and so, attuned to the lack of pursuing noises, I started hearing the dialogue between the radio and the girl from a floor somewhere above.

Seventh floor,

The ice-box and the glacier

A radio programme coming from a nearby apartment: *could emerge in coming years as global warming forces the country's glaciers to retreat. Alpine authorities have registered a significant increase in the number of human remains where*

And a girl's voice, from the same apartment: 'That's the way I found it, and I had looked for it everywhere, honest. For weeks on end the thought 'I must find it' never really left my mind, I used to wake at night with a new idea, 'maybe there, there I haven't looked.' Still, I had all but given up on it then.'

Radio: *unexpected find for the young French alpinist as he approached the summit of Mont Blanc. Poking out of the ice and snow on the shoulder of western Europe's highest mountain was a metal box containing precious gems – including emeralds, rubies and*

Girl: 'Ha! Well, not in my ice-box, no treasure there. But do I know where... One day the lift is in for repairs I'll have a look at that pit, 'cause I can almost hear the treasure sing from down below and I see the rings and coins and stuff that slips down there, have for years.'

Now, this was a bit much. I pieced it together, the singing, the voice coming from the elevator, the radio, and wondered if all these machines were indeed talking to me. Or if there was some filmed joke going on here, prompting us to listen and to care, or at least to go find the treasure buried under the elevator. I made my camera face and rushed towards the elevator doors to force them open, they were tightly shut. I only caught a glimpse of the empty dark beyond them – while radio and girl were still talking to each other somewhere near – when Gary grabbed me, with unusual strength, pulled me back violently then pushed me up the next flight of stairs.

Radio: *'can say the climber who made this find is someone very honest,' local gendarme chief Sylvain Merly said*

Girl: 'Of course he is, what do you expect? Honesty is key, in finds such as ours.'

Gary's behaviour was insane, but my own sanity concerned me more. A low metallic voice spoke out. Two, actually. Or one, but bi-fold. From the elevator.

Eight floor,

Contentment

To improve by all means at the disposal of technique the living conditions of the people, and to create a language of architectural forms, which, being firmly based on the aesthetics of our age, conveys the optimistic message of our time – the century of the common man

close to the bird's high fever,

loud in his hope and anger,

erect about his skeleton,

stands the expressive lover,

stands the deliberate man

architecture can be a potent weapon, a committed driving force on the side of enlightenment, aiming however indirectly at the transformation of our present make-believe society, where images outstrip reality and rewards outpace achievement

the friend, the rash, the enemy,

the essayist, the able,

able at times to cry.

Ninth floor,

Tell me the truth about love

I felt more alert. And some relief. I've nothing against an elevator quoting Auden and (my guess) Lubetkin. Reality puts literature to the test sooner or later, and Auden's poetry seems to be all set for the task. Artificial, ancient and direct, his poetry puts my realities to the test – exacerbating the need to listen, to the flower's soundless hunger, and to feel, the tree's clandestine tide. And the need to say, concisely, something, say one thing that may ring true for someone. Even if just a name.

'Loveless,' I said.

'Bravo,' answered Gary, whose irony spoke many languages. He was squatting down, back against the wall, and had been looking at me, squinting his eyes in a curious way this time.

'I am. Now. Loveless,' I went on, rather slowly 'Gary. I have been in love, quite recently, very much. Much grief, too. The woman – it was hard, beautiful, hurtful. In the last months, I could not remember her name. Every time I thought of her, another name would come to my mind. Every time, in our last months, that is, all the way until we broke up her name escaped me. Our love was the world to me, and I was determined not to protect myself, only be open, love her, suffer. I just realised, right this minute I swear, that by taking her name away, I was fighting her. Even now, it is the other name that comes to me, I have to make an effort to remember hers.'

'Names can be powerful spells,' he told me.

I much hoped my story sounded true to Garret.

Doors, opening.

Came the voice of the elevator, whose doors weren't opening.

'It's when you feel you are open, that is the moment you have to open up really,' said Gary, beckoning to the elevator while climbing up the stairs, the last flight of stairs. 'It is when people allow you to care that the hard work begins. And make no mistake, and this you can learn from your jesus fucking christ, most of what will come in through your open door won't be love but pain, like in a drop-in centre, yeah, enough pain to stuff your entire body with. And yet you'll have to find more room for more pointless, stupid pain.'

Tenth floor,

The phone call

He said it reaching the tenth floor's landing, and he went straight to the phone hanging from the far wall. A heavy-duty phone with no dials. Someone must have answered, on the other side of the line, after only a short time. Gary didn't give his name or the address, simply reported the malfunctioning lift. Broken lift, he said, he didn't say malfunctioning, nor elevator. He repeated it, a couple of times, in a low and pressing voice, he said it was unacceptable, and urgent that they repair it. He hung up then, moved to the centre of the landing, opened the ceiling trapdoor I hadn't noticed, grabbed the bottom end of the folded ladder and pulled it down.

'There,' he said. 'Now it's time.'

'Count your money, little cunt' he added.

He climbed up the ladder. Music, again, possibly the

elevator, dying away in the background. I stepped onto the ladder and I too reached the attic – *what we've been shown, we're living by your rules, that's all what we know. I tried to get to you…*

Attic,

Dark

Pitch dark. I follow the noise of his footsteps, they are slow but eager and don't suggest I could stop and turn on the phone's torch. So we move in the dark, crouching down – me at least, because I don't know if the ceiling is high or low, if there's stuff that hangs from it – and pacing with sentient feet because there is rubble and who-knows-what scattered on the floor. I am not sure I am following Gary, and anyway how can he know where he's going? Then I feel we are walking side by side, our shoulders almost touching. I hear a thump that seems several meters away and I wonder who the third person could be, or what could have made that noise, or what could be moving next to me in the dark.

I would say we move in circles now. Calling out, though, is out of the question. I saw the light coming in from the trapdoor, how it seemed self-contained in its open square, I am quite certain that the voice would resonate in the mouth only, confined within my teeth and I couldn't take that right now. I follow, nothing, in silence. I lose my balance and fall back on my ass. Maybe the same happened to Gary, because now that I am sitting down there is no noise around me. There are noises, gradually I make them out – as if my ears and not my eyes were adapting to the dark. But no one is moving, that's what I mean.

Water is the first noise. I hadn't heard it until now. Water dripping into water, irregularly, water on a hollow metal surface, fast and regular. It rained earlier on, I almost forgot. It was quick but thick rain, a front of cold drops sliding across like a curtain, clear with light, too. A bang now, a loud bang. And a metallic echo, possibly down the elevator pit. Singing to other stranded sailors sir. Somebody, running up the stairs. Silent again. Dark still. Not cold. I don't move a finger. The smell, also very distinct, I can't describe it now. Metal, rust, dust, of course. Scorched motor oil, maybe, maybe not. Fresh wood, definitely. Altogether fresh, alive. A hissing sound, like pressure released from a pipe. Ticking silence again. A hand on my shoulder. My shoulder lifts with it and I'm standing. This way we walk in a straight line till we come up to a wall. No one talks. I wouldn't dream of it. The hand should be Gary's, but how would I know? The hand moves to take my arm, stretches out my arm and finds a hole in the wall with it and puts my hand in it.

I have to press my face against the wall to get my hand to the far end of the hole. A smooth surface, not against my face, but where my fingers move now. Curved, hollow volumes. The bugger, this must be it. The oval. I'm running my fingers on the reverse of the moulding at the top of the Loveless façade. What our bet was about. The two figures, are they two saints, then, or one, or workers, comrades? Their arms are raised, I can feel that. They could be dancing, protesting or rejoicing, really. I'm breathing the coarse concrete wall. What better way to remember someone, something, than to breathe it in. One arm is raised and one goes around the other's waist. The arms seem to touch, gently, touch one another to find it there, the force to endure. Proletarians or saints, I would say these two are lovers, or have been, in ways they will not cease to be.

These impressions won't settle our bet. But the hand that guided my arm is not on my arm any longer. I turn my face, as much as I can with the arm deep into the hole, and in the dark I see no one is here – whoever was here must have gone and here I am, arm in the hole. A thought crosses my mind: this is how it works, one guardian must find a new one in order to be freed and maybe I just fell into the old trap. I don't believe it, really, of course, but I don't mind the idea. I almost promise I will guard these four arms touching in the oval at the top of the Loveless House, the loveless doorman, caretaker, me, and I take my arm back.

Hop-On Hop-Off London
Wolfgang Lehrner

The Simple way to see London

Stopping for a quick layover or want to get the most out of your time in London?

There's no greater way to see the best bits of the city than a hop-on hop-off bus in London.

Hop-on and off as much as you like, or complete a whole loop for a fantastic overview of the city on an open top bus.

See the city your way, with a specific point of view: the one of someone who, to summarise it brutally, is part of London and, at the same time, will never be.

This is achieved by taking all images from a strange distance but well known Google-Street-View angle.

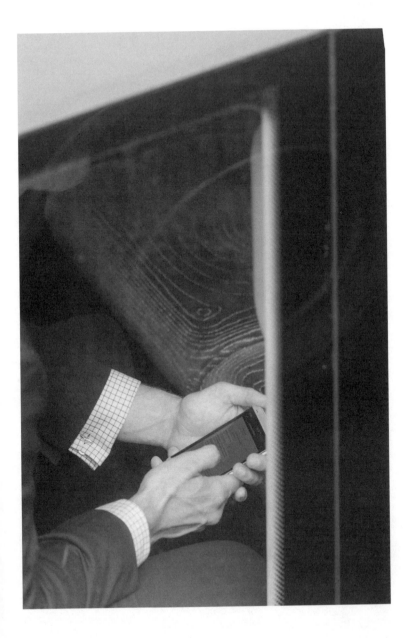

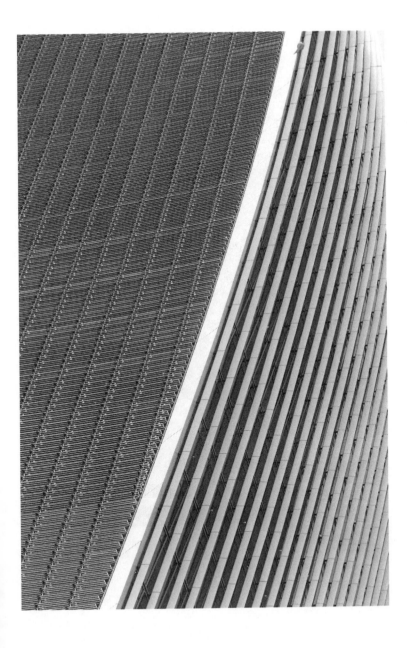

Contributors

XIAOLU GUO is a London based novelist, essayist and filmmaker. Named as a *Granta's* Best of Young British Novelist in 2013, she has published several novels and non fictions both in English and in Chinese. Her novels include *A Concise Chinese English Dictionary For Lovers* (shortlisted for the Orange Prize 2007), *Village Of Stone* (nominated for the Independent Foreign Fiction Prize) and *I Am China*. Her memoir *Once Upon A Time In The East* won the National Book Critics Circle Award 2018, and shortlisted for the Costa Book Award, RSL Ondaatje Award and Folio Prize. Her most recent novel is *A Lover's Discourse* (2020). She is also an award wining film director. Her feature film *She, A Chinese* received the Golden Leopard Award at the Locarno Film Festival. She had her film retrospectives at the Swiss Cinematheque (2010) and London's Whitechapel Gallery (2019). She is currently a writer in residence at Columbia University in New York.

VIOLA DI GRADO is an Italian author with works published in thirteen countries. With her first novel *70% Acrylic 30% Wool* she became the youngest winner of Italy's prestigious Premio Campiello Opera Prima and the youngest finalist for the Premio Strega. Her novel *Hollow Heart* was nominated for the International Dublin Literary Award and was shortlisted for the PEN Literary Awards.

SALEH ADDONIA is a London-based Eritrean-Ethiopian writer. Addonia has published a short story collection *She is Another Country* in Italian, translated by Nausikaa Angelotti. He has published short stories online such as the Italian newspapers' Il Sole 24 Ore www.specimen.press (Switzerland), www.zammagazine.com (Belgium). www.viceversaliteratur.ch (Switzerland).

CHLOE ARIDJIS is the author of three three novels— *Book of Clouds, Asunder,* and *Sea Monsters*— and was a guest curator at Tate Liverpool. In 2014 she was awarded a Guggenheim Fellowship and, more recently, the Eccles Centre & Hay Festival Writers Award. Chloe is a member of XR WRITERS REBEL and is particularly interested in issues involving animal welfare.

VANNI BIANCONI was born in Locarno (Switzerland) in 1977 and lives in London.

He published four poetry collections in Italian. His poems, translated into various languages, have been published in book form, magazines and anthologies. He was awarded the Schiller Prize, the Tirinnanzi Prize, the Marazza Prize for his translation of W.H. Auden, and was shortlisted for the European Poet of Freedom Prize 2016. In 2016 he published his first prose book in English, *London as a Second Language*. He's the founder and artistic director of the Babel, festival of literature and translation of Bellinzona, www.babelfestival. com, and of the multilingual web-magazine "Specimen. The Babel Review of Translations", www.specimen.press

JOANNA WALSH is a writer, artist and editor. She is the author of seven books including the digital work seed-story.com. Her latest book, *Break.up*, was published by Semiotext(e) and Tuskar Rock in 2018. She is a UK Arts Foundation Fellow.

ZINOVY ZINIK is a Moscow-born author who has been living in London since 1976. His recent fiction in English include *History Thieves* (2010) and *Sounds Familiar or The Beast of Artek* (2016). Since 1990s his books have also been published in Russia.

SUSANA MOREIRA MARQUES is a writer and an award-winning journalist based in Lisbon. Her work has appeared in The Guardian, Granta, Tin House, Lettre International and many other publications. She lived in London in between 2005 and 2010, where she was part of the BBC World Service while also working as a correspondent for Portuguese newspaper Público. Her non-fiction book, *Now and at the Hour of our Death*, was praised as a genre-busting debut and was translated into English, French and Spanish.

WOLFGANG LEHRNER was born in Vienna in 1980, he lives and works in Vienna and London.

Lehrner's images are marked by the observation of certain urbane, from the spaces between them, and from the resulting global transformability. Cosmopolitan in his investigations, Lehrner responds to the change and the importance of affinity apparently insignificant, consciously using coincidence to determine the direction of de-shores without destination, and their streets, roads, squares and places. The result is cinematic portraits of everyday urban life.

INFLUX
PRESS

Influx Press is an independent publisher based in London, committed to publishing innovative and challenging literature from across the UK and beyond. Formed in 2012, we have published titles ranging from award-nominated fiction debuts and site-specific anthologies to squatting memoirs and radical poetry.

Lifetime supporters: Bob West and Barbara Richards

www.influxpress.com
@Influxpress

WITH THE

Offal
Eaters

POEMS BY
DOUGLAS HOUSTON

BLOODAXE BOOKS

ISBN 0 906427 70 3

First published 1986 by
Bloodaxe Books Ltd,
P.O. Box 1SN,
Newcastle upon Tyne NE99 1SN.

This book is published with the financial support
of the Welsh Arts Council.

Bloodaxe Books Ltd acknowledges
the financial assistance of Northern Arts.

Typesetting by Bryan Williamson, Swinton, Berwickshire.

Printed in Great Britain by
Tyneside Free Press Workshop Ltd, Newcastle upon Tyne.

For Sam and Iggy

Acknowledgements

Acknowledgements are due to the editors of the following publications in which some of these poems have appeared: *Bananas*, *Communicon*, *New Poetry 9* (Hutchinson/Arts Council — P.E.N., 1983), *Outcrop*, *Poetry Review*, *Poetry Supplement* (Poetry Book Society, Christmas 1979), *Quarto*, *Spectrum*, *Stone Ferry Review*, *To Build a Bridge* (Lincolnshire & Humberside Arts, 1982), and the *Western Mail*. 'Ward Seven' was broadcast on *Calendar Carousel* (Yorkshire Television).

Sixteen poems from this collection appeared in Douglas Dunn's anthology *A Rumoured City: new poets from Hull* (Bloodaxe Books, 1982).

Contents

To the Management

I have used your buses for eighteen years.
The day after the new rubber bands came
It occurred to me to write to you.
I was examining an orange pippin
Beneath my desk lamp. Flecks of red
Like dabs of bird's blood grew dense on one side,
The other bald and green. A wonderful sight.
Why not fix small lamps on the seat backs
For people to examine their fruit carefully?
Wash-hand basins should be provided;
Some who use your services are not clean.
I enclose my design which incorporates
A pillar box and cigarette machine.
Your buses should stop outside our houses;
Most of us live on roads of some sort.
A change of colour would be welcome.
Margaret and I thought a shade of lilac.
Personally, I'd appreciate some facility
For heating the tea-cosy I wear on my head,
Which could certainly be put to other uses.

Devotions

Having mortified myself with a hangover,
Deliberately conceived on two days' hard drinking,
I am standing underneath the end of the pier
In the year's high ritual of my seagull worship,
Which demands such unbreakfasted, humbling rigours,
And will culminate with prostration in the surf
After the solemn dispensation of breadcrusts.

A friend, long of the behaviourist persuasion,
Calls worship a proper respect got out of hand,
The mystery of the gulls beyond his dissections
To trace why what is done is done just as it is —
A closed-circuit, tape-loop mentality to me,
Only to be envied the comfort of closed doors
And confidence in the given human reasons.

He laughs at the Botanical Salvationists
Whose resurrection is the pot-plant of one's choice,
But I'd become a *nephrolepis exaltata*
Sooner than a name unsought in some register,
And their watering rites have great delicacy.
I have given him a pectoral of feathers,
And wait for him to bow, like the dove, to the gull.

I have time for Devotees of Telegraph Poles.
Sighting along their black totems at certain stars,
They believe light is soluble in midnight rain,
That high winds snatch beams from outlying farmhouses
And anglers' lamps, then mix the stuff into wet air,
Which the poles absorb to transmit the stars their light.
A simple religion, but lacking daylight truth.

I have risen now, soaked and icily refreshed,
From the white fringes of the sea where I have lain
The required fifteen minutes. Their cries above me
Worked sacred hypnosis, each mew a blade of truth.
Some of the sand from my clothes and skin will be kept
To be rubbed in my beard every Monday, run through
My fingers daily until next year's renewal.

10

Cycle

The floor of the court of judgement splits.
The judge is jarred awake and cries
'There are specific gravities to be considered!'
The dust of the destruction drifts,
Germinates order among the primitives
Emerging from vegetable ease
On sundry planets. Men resembling men
Begin to notice their shadows,
Occur to themselves in separate forms
From which the lexicons develop
Until the pod of structure bursts.
The floor of the court of judgement splits.

Another Time

'Another time has other lives to live'
W.H. AUDEN

The fantastic balloons broke free of their moorings,
Making coloured havoc in an inky sky.
Light aircraft attempted to herd them together.
In sunlight that came through beneath the building cloud
The fields we ran across were bright as summer makes them,
And scattered with bone-white tribes of mushrooms.
The eruption of smoke that filled
A quarter of the horizon
Formed into no shape of demon,
But rose to swell its own ascending turbulence.

A country where little boys were called *master*
Failed to meet the last blackmail payment.
A body politic dissolved into the world.
Some of its lighter pieces we brought here with us;
Ambition is purely local now
Interest has lost its sense of direction,
And only necessity really remains.
We made glass by melting sand.
Blotched and coarse, it admits light.
Here by the ocean I glean mussels from the rocks.

Sic Transit

The glory of the world is passing already
With white blossoms dropping from the may's laden boughs.
The heels of the man with shattered kneecaps crush them
To a moist translucency. Dead prisoners gather
On the green outside the Methodist Hall to hear
A moving address on human rights delivered
By a visiting Belgian milkman, who breaks down
When whispers inform him of a lost football match.
People who happened to be listening to radios
Maintained their politic silence while descending
To shelters now crowded and firmly closed.

Beethoven's Fifth

There will be quiet after all these deaths,
When all the toppled headstones turn to light.
The trumpet's blast takes all the angel's breath
Before he drops it laughing at the sight
Of every face distraught with hope and fear;
And suddenly the dance of heaven breaks out
With huge benevolence and peasant cheer,
All war and anger gathered in a shout
That burns itself out brightly in deep space,
While wheeling in ascent the dance expands,
All movement lit to speed by cosmic grace.
The galaxies without cannot withstand
This nebula's attraction as it grows.
All light tracks in. A single body glows.

The Last Waltz

Death underwrites their music's dignity,
The bogey-man of living on the road
That lends their rock its dark alacrity,
A music turned by men who know what's owed.
Their genial modesty does not preclude
The litany of Janis, Jimi, Brian;
The doped eyes' morbid twinkle only proves
If they're not dead, it's not for want of trying.

When Dylan comes on ripping songs to bits
The cognoscenti aren't in any doubt
He's doing it because they once were hits,
Which justifies his nasal torture-bouts.
This is the way the *Abendland* goes down,
The lamp's flame spitting in its mirror's eye;
There's no one worth a flattering glance in town,
Though somehow hirsute millionaires get by.

Then just to prove it's all about salvation,
He tunes his voice for 'I Shall Be Released',
The universal prisoner's declaration
Giving this evening's sense of ending peace.
The slow refrain is raised by rock musicians,
Steel-driving rhythms eased to navigate
The waters of prospective manumission
Where history and hard-travelling terminate.

Tomorrow Never Knows
(i.m. John Lennon, 1940-1980)

No guilt attaches to a hero's end;
Five bullets from a madman's gun defend
The right to sudden death that cities keep
For those whose truth disturbs official sleep.

There was blue sky unclouded by belief.
The clarity of daylight was enough.
A man was singing of the one relief
That life affords from death and he meant love.

Ward Seven

(for Bill Cooper)

Lurching out of anaesthetics
On tubular Health Service beds,
Some will now require prosthetics
Or bags that drip to keep them fed.

Counting trains and feeding pigeons,
An amputee can still react
To the world that once he lived in
Before he signed the standard pact:

More years, less pain, terms understood
For his abridgement at mid-thigh;
No clause, though knives and wills are good,
Can guarantee that no one dies.

Each beyond his own salvation,
Their democratic suffering breeds
A politics of supplication:
To each according to his needs . . .

Mr W.

Propped by his bone structure in a chair,
Dope from the last bout of raving fixes him.
A mop avoids his one and black-toed foot.
He is uttering a private language
Of articulate mumbles, a long plaint
Whose undulations seem to plead sometimes,
Then level into planes of easy chat.
He has a little English for the nurse,
Who shaves him, then conceals the charcoal toes
With bandage, pulls a white sock on the stump.

Lights out, and his urgent whispers draw me
Into the landscape of his latest fear,
A valley where the Russians mobilise
Somewhere beyond the dark end of the ward;
Lie low, the only feasible strategy,
As the notion fades and the nurses come
To wheel him to a side room where his cries
Against the next régime of paranoia
Will not uproot light sleepers from their rest.

After the Anaesthetic

A baby eating spiders,
Over-boiled capsicum slices on surgical lint,
A brown toad with a young newt on its back,
The sun blurred on a bright bicycle wheel.
A bath that drains to leave a silt of marijuana,
Los Angeles glimpsed from a banking aircraft,
A fountain pen with a mutating nib
That moves through every plane and angle
Small rectangular plates of gold.
The space that fills the barrel of a gun
Removed from its metal context.
A man who finds living a nuisance
And is depressed there's nothing else to do,
Whose wife embodies smiling patience,
Looks beautiful and young,
Unlike his Belsen legs and mute philosophy.
A headless man in a brown dressing-gown
Sits comfortably in a wheelchair.
Courtly barbarian giants dressed in plum velvet
And leopard skins laugh and surround the throne
On which sits a ramshackle structure of beams and cloth.
A young spiral's bravura of energy in blue space.
Northerly seascapes tilt silver levels of sunlight.
My hands produce a perfect golf-ball on a potter's wheel.
Bonsai pines in souvenir clogs
Wave in deep sub-aqueous currents
While memory explains the nature of guilt
In cold parables of love and injury.

For My Father

Thirty-two, I approach the age
You were when, sole survivor,
Passive hero of a torpedoing,
You floated with a timber
In the North Atlantic night.
Out of hypnotic hours of sea you turn,
And the young seaman with you has gone.

The tanker shocked into frantic last activity,
You hammered out the S-O-S.
Now searchlights rotate from rescue boats.
You sink beneath a scanning beam
On rollers close to cancelling my birth.
You tell it rarely, baffled and amused
By your confidence that you'd be all right.

Next, you are in photographs,
Business-suited at conferences, exhibitions,
Your posed smiles alive with enthusiasm
Of the 'fifties, pleased with electric shavers,
Televisions and stereophonic sound.
Dutch bosses styled you 'King of Scotland';
Glasgow and you were on good terms.

Then company policy sent you to London,
Balham's executive anonymity
Galling. Our differences came of age,
Flammable as napalm. Hippy waywardness
Provoked you to wars of ideology.
You retired. I gave up long hair and beads.
The underlying friendship supervened.

And suddenly you're almost old in Wales,
Eighty miles from your native Cardiff.
Dyfed's hills suit your hard-bitten happiness.
The world having ceased to bother you much,
Its ports of your sea years and its business
Fund you with tales worth hearing more than once.
A life away, I can almost touch you.

'Here's tae Us . . .'

This was my father's tankard,
Truncated cone of pewter, glass
Through which light strikes the bay of beer
At the bottom of which lies emptiness.
The handle's bow and his masonic fist
Were intimate where my mother served the beer,
In Cardiff in the old days when the trams ran,
Say 1945, before my time.

Out of retirement now, it holds home-brew,
A pint and a slop on top at a time,
And that passes well through the guts of a son
Who thinks as he drinks of a father months gone
Since the summer that suddenly turned on a funeral
Has itself been disposed of in due season,
And the norms of wetness, wind and cold
Are re-established in this muddy shire,
In which he died, that now assumes his flesh.

Comatose, he hung on till the doctor came,
Then punctually ceased to struggle for breath.
I have come into much since that day, his birthday,
When we ate his chocolates more thoughtfully
Than chocolates are usually eaten,
And though I regret not kissing the body
At my sister's request, for both of us,
Our lips meet out of time round this tankard.

Remembrance Day Photograph

Two old men at an empty tomb,
Faintly grinning their memories' grimness
On a November afternoon
Forty years since the Japanese
Imprisoned Jones who holds the flag
And Houston floated in the sea
For hours somewhere south of Iceland.

So Jones came home, like many didn't,
The searchlight found Houston in the swell
Alone of those off *W.C. Teagle*,
And each grew old among the hills,
Both with three medals for their black coats,
A certain honour in the parish,
Where farmers live who never went to war.

I saw Jones in his mini today,
Hail his son on the road sometimes,
Though all I see of Houston is a mound
That waits to settle till it has its stone.
The years of prison, the torpedo's moment,
Have stamped these gazes worth revering
For all the profit of what medals mean.

In Llanybydder

(in memory of N.D. Houston)

On nights like this when the wind swirls rain
In sudden arabesques on the road's shining surface
As the car penetrates the drenching fusillade
And the landscape labours on through sodden time,
When weeks of such weather reach a foul epitome
And I cannot reach my love by telephone,
I pass an hour in the bar we used to drink in,
Father, preferring the company of strangers to my own,
And I think how wet the cemetery must be,
Conceiving of death as utter, boxed loneliness
On the side of the hill above the river,
Just up from the slaughterhouse, its stench
From the skip full of guts drowned out
In the wet lashing your headstone is taking.
By now I suppose I'd shudder to see you,
After a year in that filled-in hole,
But how deep your absence goes on nights like this
When my solitude alive and yours in death
Coincide where memory meets the moment
As the rain rains on and on into winter
And each bad day helps me catch up with you.

Holly

The waxen berries are red as fresh blood,
Arterially bright, as comparison proved
When a green-vellum leaf pricked one of its cusps,
Sharp and minute, thorn-hard at the tips,
Into a finger of the hand that plucked it.

My night raid where I'd spotted the good branches
Was quickly planned down to breadknife and torch.
Light was indispensable as I climbed
The dozen feet to where the tree grew whole;
Below, the council's blades had hacked it hedge-flush.

Stuffed in my tight-buttoned jacket, the torch
Obeyed, after practice, my strangely mobile chest,
But half-way up the knife and the tree
Entertained homicidal conspiracy.
The blade stayed unneeded in my back pocket,

The soft twigs I wanted coming away
With a snap and a rustle that lost a few berries.
This morning I noticed the fine red striations,
Like traces of a tiny rodent's scratching,
Hatched on one hand at the base of the thumb;

A small price, with the drop or two the leaf took,
Resentful at being stuck above a mirror,
For the cursory belief in prosperity
That the berries confer on another year's prospect,
A scarlet crop of luck, though not as lustrous

As the lacquered sheen of the topsides of leaves,
Reducing the room to a blurring of light
Caught on the tensile waves of their scallopings.
Of the fictions of metal that trees can conjure
The subtlest and richest might be these twigs' bark,

With powdered gold compounded in the green
That will not take a name, though turned in light
Until I meet the roots of superstition,
This gazing that no longer wants a reason,
Bound to its object, become its own rite.

D.T.s on the Königsallee

The indiscretion of your shakes disgusts
The street. German propriety tolerates
Tipsiness — gentlemen may wobble here.
But you, squarely slumped at a corner,
Wholly wild, have gone too far for *der Kö*
They fondly call their Champs Elysées.
Here eyes assume a brief familiarity
With gold in frequent jewellers' windows,
Rich whims pass by in crocodile-skin boots —
Lives of narcissistic polish cannot
Contain the raw reflection you present,
Staring past the world, charmed in horror
At this state, some cardboard box you've come by
Forgotten alongside, irrelevant as a shave
In the tremoring shock of your moment,
Almost empty anyway. They look aside
With flinches more pronounced than usual,
Your *tremens* rhythm manic and far out
Of time and place, the Deutsche Mark Concerto
Interpreted here in leisurely movements
Of suave entrepreneurs, *fortissimo*
Of black Porsches controlled by lights
At every bridge across the ornate Düssel —
Jump in it, you blistering anomaly;
Would they break step for a drowning dipso?
You must be gone soon. Help you need badly
Is not here. The police will come no doubt
And see to that. Meanwhile you are too real,
A stain on silk underpants, noxious — their
Rémy Martin would turn in your presence.
Have some pfennigs, the price of no drink,
A stinting grant for a happening like you,
Grim object-lesson, labelled 'Past It All'.

Horst Wessel on Alcatraz

My lookalike passed muster in the morgue.
I left him my name. They took up the song
That impelled the metronomic goosestep
Down boulevards rippling red and black.
Disappearing quickly was expensive;
New papers and a passage fixed in Köln,
I left others to arrange the details:
The gutter nexus of crime and politics
Accepted a nominal sacrifice.
War was building while I learned American
In cinemas across the States. Newsreels
Amazed me with my name, in Denver first
In 'thirty-three; the Reich's chief martyr, me,
A nameplate on this anthem's powerhouse;
What slender pretexts art seems to require.
I got to 'Frisco, organised some girls,
Was doing well but crossed the wrong people.
That day the splintering door was no surprise.
I'd slept with the Schmeisser all week; one burst
From under the bed-clothes finished them.
I wasted time cleaning their billfolds out;
The cops were in before I'd tied my shoes.

Three paces cross this cell at its widest.
Maybe the first year is the worst: I cracked,
Fought warders and was thrown in the hole.
After days on slops in total darkness
I couldn't tell sleep from being awake.
That song became the music of nightmares.
I begged, like guys do sooner or later;
Stark naked, I crawled when they let me out.
The warders who know I'm German taunt me
With the war — as if it was my damn' fault.
Dense mist blanks out the bay again tonight.
The seagulls and foghorns sound like lost souls.
To the flat rhythm of patrolling steps
My tune is whistled on the next landing.

The Layman Considers the Gods of Place

What of the gods of place? Are they no more
Than rumoured reasons for how men behave?
If real they've got a lot to answer for,
Like crying 'Havoc' while Herr Hitler raved
Until the *Deutsches Volk* latched on to myth
So zealously that all good sense was sunk,
Jack-booted *lethe* seeping from the pith
Of fabled boughs that crazed them power-drunk,
Until their local hatred quickly seized
Upon the feared and dark minorities.
The Irish *dei loci* aren't good news;
The ethnic's heady brew when times are tough.
What native peace place does afford's abused
Till, blood-sick, gods at last cry out 'Enough!'

Case History

A mobile childhood stunted my knowledge
Of the rites of inherited hatred
Taught on an extra-curricular basis
When Orange songs and Jew-baiting oppressed
The convenient playground minorities.

My bluffing betrayed lack of conviction,
So I gave up and lived right off the tracks
On which heavy opinions run through lives.
My behaviour lacked that regulation
That comes from aggression and self-interest.

The hospital appealed for a while.
I was adequate to its routine of lawns,
Early rising, and psychotic mischief
Within the pale of the merit system,
Till flower-pot throwing pricked its thick hide.

After six months I had gone down two wards
To regions where the mumbling people lived,
Steered round all day by bored male nurses,
And remembering themselves occasionally
In fits of violent indignation.

Escape required I convince the doctors
By toeing the line of sanity nicely
In carefully relaxed conversations
By which I graduated out of there.
The world posed all the usual questions.

My friend and I met in the cemetery,
She gleaning groundsel from the scrubby verges,
My plastic bag half-full of kindling twigs.
We did what people do and called it love.
I will not tell you where we live, or how.

From the Corner

'Think thou on hell Faustus, for thou art damned.'

When I go out an unscrupulous doctor
Performs operations in my bath.
Like bits of red fluff, traces of viscera
Bob to my soapy ribs. This knowledge
Accounts for losses, movements of my things.

Although the bricks tolerate me,
Tonight the doors are breathing hard.
These spots on my face are crude attempts
By the insect population to plant
Their sensors in my skin. I root them out.

The trees are in a conspiracy
Spanning millions of years
And all things carboniferous,
Drawing an aeon of breath before they advance.
Vegetarian DJs in their pay

Insinuate details of my secret life
Into their broadcasts of gloating trash.
While I doze, my wife tears down wallpaper;
I come to and find her pretending to read.
Like my friends, she is one of the police.

The public, dead keen on hangings,
Are anxious to have me sized up.
From two gardens away a telescope
Is trained on my penis
Through a gap in cherry-red curtains.

Version

*'This has nothing to do with history, which is
the circle's after-image of itself exploited for
private ends'* — W.H. AUDEN

The simplified past is containable,
Explicable, the handy version
Of what happened to each
Man or nation, interest and necessity
Rendered as the right thing done.

The propaganda minister who dies
Believing his own lies, the clown
Who raises a death-bed chuckle,
Fanatics terminally wired to God,
Gratify a sense of order.

Legends of beauty or heroism,
Keats and Nelson exquisitely inlaid
Upon the journeywork of their age,
Are bright handles to the coffin of history,
Dovetailed with significant dates.

The tight weave of facts frays at the edges
Into the spaces between works of reference.
Learning and opinion set their limits
By positing caricatures of truth.
Astronomers scan the straight record's source.

Nighttown Revisited

Amid a squalor of cracked plates,
Large dogs and filthy lavatories,
Chaplin is on television
Fluttering his timid politesse.
Such innocence has escaped unnoticed
Through the gaps in loosening brickwork.

Garish capsules of barbiturate
Are palmed, glanced at and swallowed,
Intoxication in the barest terms,
Like the needle's indecent exposure.
Articulation wears thick rubber gloves,
Fumbles with its predictable matter.

Summonses and writs displayed over beer
By way of introduction, a stranger
Laconically disapproves of
The stabbing of a one-armed man.
Uneasy and accepted here, I know
Simplicities of crime and chronic need.

Night of the Lion

Only a straw of light beneath the door
Disturbs the darkness. The pitted square bars
Might be by Eiffel, a heavy tracery
Of iron, a cage within this corridor
At the end of which the beast finds the ring.

It is warm in here, and the high unease
Of coming has passed in well-lit comfort.
The lion's entrance is imminent now
And the night is distraught with waiting.

I have been in love's confidence sometimes,
Seen the beauty she kept for a husband
In glimpses after eight unmarried years.
A hurtling card can unbalance a life.
It will all have been worthwhile at the end.

Next to Godliness

I move slowly in my porcelain boat
On a turquoise sea, the grosser pleasures
Forsaken for this intercourse with light.
Golden exactitude governs all measures
Here; I am at one with doing nothing,
And act only upon the most complete
Inspirations. Look — yesterday I made
This small ivory box. Flawless. Replete
With the peace I once pursued with morbid
Assiduity, I finger the dust
From old intentions and failures to show
Their cracked brightness I had taken on trust.
Returned, I drip and shiver for my shirt,
Leaving the bath its silt of votive dirt.

Travelling Musician

Recalling the details fascinates me.
I see the beach where my wife and I fought,
The bedded hulks, the ocean behind us.

She went. Grief splayed like sprung steel. I wallowed
In snow, got scotch in a cheap painted glass.
My Catholic grandmother had one like that.

I dabbled a while in patent medicine.
Speciously worded, the labels' fine print
And credulous faces are crisp as stamps.

Nothing is really forgotten; I played
In cinemas, on pavements everywhere,
Four strings vibrant round the core of a song.

I played where the best whores danced — such slit skirts!
Such well-propped breasts! Some money was easy,
But most of it came slowly in small coin.

Of my several wives, each beautiful,
One made good bread, another played the drums.
The note I was is fading to a pause.

The Music Man

Cats who have heard me have turned into eels,
The flexings of their bodies reaching
To the trembling point of an outstretched claw.

Vegetation sighs in silent expansion
Of the green mass of each leaf and frond
When jungles hear my yearning notes.

Stone has been known to ring exultance
When I have let the usual sound escape
In ancient sites gods or volcanoes ruined.

An end in itself, my pipe brings no good,
A proof that sheer amazement profits nothing,
Although, like sleep, it leaves a blank for dreams.

I have learned there is an end to music,
Some note the stars depend on which when played
Undoes the bond that holds the sky in place.

The tunes that I know flit like glancing light
Across the surface of that latent key
That waits coeval with the end of days.

Lines on a Van's Dereliction

'Farewell! thou art too dear for my possessing.'

This rust-infested cage with worn-out brakes,
Green paintwork scratched as if a demon clawed it,
Calls forth these tribute lines for old times' sake —
It's future's scrap, I simply can't afford it.
The engine's blown some seal that keeps the oil in,
The windows seem the only parts intact;
Though recently I screwed a brand-new coil in,
Such costly items will no more exact
The cash from me to keep it on the road.
Permit me now the vocative, O van,
Defeated by that last excessive load,
The tons of logs your brakes tried to withstand
In huge momentum down the mountainside;
For many thousand miles I've driven you,
A third-hand emblem of a sort of pride,
But now the year is 1982,
Your time, at thirteen years, is up I think.
In olive groves or by the sea we parked you,
Our four-wheeled bedroom-wine-bar-kitchen-sink;
On that first trip the Florence police remarked you
And towed you off for us to go your bail,
But recollection's pasta can't obscure
The fact that now your braking power's failed
We'd like a vehicle just a wee bit *newer*.
So farewell now old heap, have fun as tins.
One day within the geochronic system
Digesting contents of all rubbish bins
My big toe might encounter your third piston.
We'll render gaseous traces to the sky
While mineral satisfactions of the earth
Redistribute our atoms by and by.
Infinity's before us right from birth;
So don't take it too badly, rusty friend,
Should I dismember you to sell as parts;
Remember being doesn't simply end,
Disintegration's where the big time starts.

Dead Man's Shoes

The leathern strata of the best pair's heels
Had brought forth powdery sulphur-yellow mould.
But costly, sleek, of calf, I liked their feel;
His widow asked ten pounds; we called them sold.

It took eight months for grief to dissipate
Sufficiently to sell off his effects;
An invalid, the soles were in a state
That told his legs had fallen to neglect.

She'd said that he's been big, and I regret
His pants and jackets would have held me twice;
But bless his perished feet, a matching set
For my elevens, their cast-offs at a price

She took by cheque, accepting it post-dated.
The daughter fetched two more pairs from the shed,
While mother, in continuing, related
How on a snowed-up night she'd found him dead

On his return from going for a pee;
'Ten for the brand-new casuals, two for these,
Take three pairs and you'll have the slippers free'.
Furred arteries, it seems, were his disease.

I'm happy in my socks, but, *de rigeur,*
A man needs shoes to strut his stuff today.
I'm keeping those calf numbers to ensure,
If necessary, my feet will look O.K.

On Papua

Mix-master belong Jesus Christ reduced
To *helicopter* in the names he knows,
Boss-boy counts out a handful of new words.
Already he commands their pick-up truck
Bought with sacks of damp notes lugged to the showroom.
He sits next to the one who can drive,
The elect behind encamped on deck-chairs.

In a clearing they made a giant bird
Of timbers, the brightest feathers and blooms,
To tempt the silver flier down to mate.
This marriage would produce more silver bellies
Filled with radios, denims and ball-point pens.
Two years' rains stripped the wooden skeleton.
It became a feature of the jungle.

In Lae men died on zebra crossings
From excessive faith in white-man's magic.
The sea no longer awes him or his men
As when they squatted silent on the beach
Witnessing the fact of tribal legend.
Far out there, Boss-boy knows, is *Base of Heaven*,
Where every home is full of manifest truth.

The House Party

The deck-chairs balloon to their burdens, endure
Vacuity of July afternoons,
Until, after six, the breeze hints at night,
Plays riffling chords on newspapers and trees.
Sweet as nostalgia, British white wine
Makes the blunt uncle dream of the Derby;
The epic trance of the last furlong's roar
Wakes him to the queer surprise of chill.

Broken by language's complicity
In defamation of the beautiful myths,
The loyalist poet has turned misanthropic.
From the belvedere's quaint green solipsism
He tries to write himself out of the world.
The gardener dismissed for reading Borges
And dressing as a gaucho on days off,
The old consensus dominates these acres.

Untended, briars arch into anarchy
Along the rose-walk where dowagers revise
Hereditary codices of rumour.
Croquet is becoming impossible;
The Major-General has a ruthless plan.
Chromatics of pinks, foxgloves, rhododendrons,
Flame in the arcane lesson of sunset
Through the french-windows of the billiard room,

Where such ephemerae are not accounted
By men grouped earnestly around the table
Following the fleet in an old school atlas.
In conclave with the gerontocracy
Of gnarled ancestral oaks on the west rise,
The master has learned silence and detests
Cacophonies of voices, glass and silver,
Awaits the long inheritance of trees.

The Rest

'What fills the heart is felt to make amends'
SEAN O'BRIEN

Within the bell of Sunday is this peace
The errant heart reads as a sign to kill
The living poise the day has given it,
And, blank with dedication, stagger on.
The shopkeepers at worship with their custom
Annul their differences in bread and wine,
Their voices' satisfactory intercourse
With music's ideal model of sweet time,

And it is a summer day for children,
The spring of their laughter flooding the garden
With the being of the love we cannot act,
Having learned all about days and the world,
Knowing ourselves too well to give an inch,
Yet able to acknowledge what it means
In our enduring envy of the light,
The voice's cracking reaching for that note.

Keeping our fingers crossed, we ignore pain,
But find it hard to decide what to do;
Sleep, books, drink, friendship, work, nag simple choice
Into complicity of compromise,
A bit of this fits with a bit of that,
Until intention's teleology
Insists only the end is pure at all,
Commends as righteous self-destruction's norm,

Enfranchises the knife as symbol-maker,
Its edge's mordant gesture in the flesh
A token of the justice we encode
Into the sad rococo of behaviour.
So the gasping runner reaches Arcadia
With news of the victor's new agony,
Continuing his furious duel with time,
Maddening the city with the clangorous bell.

Auto-Elegy

My morals slackened as my wit improved —
Superlative penetration assists
The central intentions of business
In hiding a persuasion or insult
Within the flash of its necessary speed.
Famous apologias for the destruction
Of my health and the peace of my parents
(Upright people, though somewhat unbalanced)
Were coined by a mind glib on its own skill.

All the time I devoted to mirrors
Paid off in perfect familiarity
With the simple idea of myself,
Tangible and cheap as the krugerrand
I bought to celebrate my first big deal.
The day Lennon died I met her, my fall
From an explicable world ordained then.
I no longer thought of situations
As matters to be governed or dismissed.
The krugerrand provided cash for toast.

Now I am in heaven where dead poets
Make aerial attacks upon bureaucrats
Forming tight squares on the white heaths of cloud.
Something gets through unfiltered
From the origin of diversity.
From here I have watched with disinterest
While ravens picked over my fallen body.

Driver

When vanity leaves me, I am truly alone.
I observe a nocent rendezvous of police cars,
Know each man a sort of wheel-gripping animal
Driving through the city's sodium-yellow A-roads,
My own compass set for the marshy coastal flats.
Out there I will be quite at ease, and shivering,
If this refrigerated summer has its way.
If I see Will o' the Wisp, I will write and tell you,
Otherwise consider my silence salutary.
Rubber soles dry, pedal contact excellent,
My headlights dust moth wings out past the town,
And cruising at sixty miles an hour I think of you,
Sweeter than all the chocolate on the road, more shapely
Than the slow curve of the highway way out here
Where they followed the solid levels on the map
To swing long waves of tarmac to the coast; almost there,
I believe I can smell the chosen patch of marsh.

Liberty

I will free the birds trapped in the plumbing;
Their twittering distresses me at midnight.
Asleep, the house creaks while its bladder fills.

Faint bleatings from the cooling kettle seem
From a distance beyond three dimensions.
I can silence these sheep by moving it.

I desire peace with the rhythm of years,
And will henceforth welcome the crystalline
Precipitate forming at the edges

Of my consciousness of breathing on clear
Winter nights when all signals are cancelled
By an open-handed lucidity.

When these things are done, my nervous habits
(Also trapped creatures of some kind) will cease
And I shall be as harmless as the dead.

Eremetic Definition

I had given up on caves; the beer cans,
Stiff green sandwiches, burnt sticks and dried shit
Were beyond my distance from the ideal.
There were tramps in some, often drunken men
Mean as dogs tethered to small territories.
Tents were no substitute, mostly day-glo
Conspicuous. Pleasant, airy-minded perhaps,
But quite lacking the gravity I need.
A house seemed the next best thing, mausolea
Too deathly grand, hostels crowded places.
Prison was considered, the moral issues wide:
Gravity and containment attractive,
Too many cohabitees ruled it out.
(It's not so much misanthropy as fear
As far as I have been able to trace
My motives in the matter of people
And their avoidance.)
Wanting a barrel, I found a large pipe,
Concrete and eight feet across. A few nights
Dissuaded me — Diogenes at least
Had one end covered, and no limy dust.
I worked for years, then bought a granite house.
The several lodgers know little of me.
Sometimes at night I hear televisions,
Laughter, the comings and goings of friends.
These small noises are enough of others.
I might yet accept a drink at Christmas.

The Conference of Anonymity

Partially concealed within pin-stripe suits,
Special pleadings for dolphins bore us.
The dots on our brogues are more interesting
Than the relative supremacy of proximate species.

Our differences too apparent, some uniform adjusts.
Their *svelte* sameness is simple unity. No wonder
Conformity is ease. We try, reach agreement
On certain points. Don't talk of bees or killer whales:

Such creatures live with the Buddha's dullness;
No sparks between them and the world at large.
Though necessary in the last analysis,
We can learn nothing from them but peace.

After all, we can confer immanence
On tins, lend barnacled stones the power
Of knowing for our own brief purposes.
Indeed, gentlemen, we have variety at our disposal.

The Others

I am not the man who sits alone
At a rustic table in a pub garden,
But as he turns his head to watch me pass
I admire his solitary love of air.

The man who always knows when leap-years are,
Whose papers are all in immaculate order,
Is more of a stranger — aloof, I suspect,
So I call him *The Pocket Book of Boredom*.

Others constitute a powerful faction;
Their numbers are not to be taken lightly
In assessing the management of a life.
Study one or two, but keep your distance.

Their variety is overwhelming.
How they united I don't know,
But the undertaker's assistant,
Tactful as rollers under a coffin,

Delicate girls who work in flower-shops,
Every Chinese person in the world,
All those who wear uniforms or nothing,
Are beyond my first person singular.

Despite occasional hostilities
By and large they have been good to me.
Lately I agree with them on many points,
Though I hear of their internal differences.

It is my hope that these will be resolved.
I'd be foolish to take this for granted,
Each of them finally in my position,
Having seen nasty behaviour, some of it mine.

Bed and the Cemetery
(for Karen)

The idle winds of early spring that draw
Gestures of vacancy from wilting flowers
Among the stone angels and disregarded mounds,
The well-dressed headstones and the leaning jamjars,
Help me to call upon a vast indifference
To hold up like a sword against my life,
Forbidding days' complexity to pass,
Meaning something beyond the fact of absence
That kneeling figures with their offerings tell of,
The husbands, wives, descendants, friends and siblings,
Like me, who came here to remember
Love's persistent ticking in the silence.
Oblivion, thought's cessation, on the grass
Above the clay that's mixed up with dear flesh,
Different in kind and quality but like
The fullness when all questioning is done
In the pauses that my love and I achieve
Beneath warm bedclothes at the day's far end,
The absoluteness of our mingled breaths
In darkness before and after the moves
That climax rushing into wordless space,
While life laps back upon a tide of peace;
And it is not just morbid to desire
Death in those moments for perfection's sake,
Subordinating everything to love,
Like headstones do, like flowers left out to die,
Insisting there is something more than life
When that has gone, that the vast spaces
Inside our souls are real and populated
By sacred abstractions attractive at last,
The unity of lovers and the dead.

Cemetery

The fairground's muted racket reaches here.
Shrieks of the loudest girls rise on the bass
Of rides, rock music and the ghost train's keen.

Beyond offence or reverence
The pure zero of immortality
Is silence to the massed rustle of leaves.

I saw two women laughing here today,
But now the sun is red amid the trees;
Evening's chill moral has tightened my jaw.

Going Downstairs

A pint too many was the step he missed,
Plunged into a fatal coincidence of angles,
His guitar's head lodging beneath his chin.
The floor's ineluctable solidity
Drove it home. The blow detonated
All he knew into uncontainable light,
Drowning him without a struggle.
Stars of fierce magnitude remained,
Pulsing their rapid ebb to nothing
As the signals from his blood stopped.

The only person he meets in the dream
Forever recurrent is Shin Adzar,
A young Malay who sucks his teeth
And sniffs gutturally between smiling,
Attentive politenesses. Obsessed
With deference to the ending
Of English third person singular verbs,
Shin adds an 's' to every word:
'Goods evenings. I'ms glads yous cames.
Happys tos findings hell's likes this?'

The Return

'Aujourd'hui l'espace est splendide'
BAUDELAIRE

The poet led me out along the quays
Where night discloses luminous desires,
Like neon leeches twitching their small fires
In cisterns of original disease.

There was no speaking in that dismal peace;
Looks asked and answered all that could be known.
The air was static as the vaulted stone
That fixed the limits where all sequence ceased.

My guide politely nodded his *adieu*,
Then, stepping into shadow, disappeared.
Escape was not as hard as I had feared;
I followed clues of light that filtered through

A dim expanse of culverts and canals.
I first saw day through grilles, then over walls;
Paved banks gave way to grass, where waterfalls
Accompanied the birds in spring chorales.

Gardens
(for Peter Didsbury)

I cross the civic lawns of Eikon Basilike
With you, their author in this ordered guise for me;
The city's maritime aspect is manifest
As scholars of sailing in their cobbled courtyard
By the dome the atmosphere makes metallic grass.
Reciprocal flatness of soil and sea dictate
A rectilinear hortulan geometry,
Each meeting of streets a square cross that determines
The parallel parcelling of demotic gardens,
Where sometimes our timetables permit us to spend
An hour or two together in summer.

Mansions dynamited decades ago, estates
Have left their rhododendron hedges purpling June
Round Ystwyth. Here gardening is not an indulgence.
In the chimney-pot's echo chamber nestlings chant
Ensemble; they are demanding life, more of it,
While I admire the grass I'm meant to scythe, the tool
Blunt and depending from a rafter in the shed.
Our neighbour constructs an isoceles skeleton
From sharpened beech staves above our bean-rows, tutting
At the bad free-verse of our planting, head shaken
At my regrettable simplicity.

The Clasp
(in memory of Lesley Dunn)

> 'They are all gone into the world of light'
> VAUGHAN

Fifty yards down the lane, your back to me,
Her Grecian hair-clasp catches the sunlight,
Its curls of hammered silver wire flashing
Amazingly on your coil of jet hair,
A bodying forth of the light that contains
The late snowdrops, primrose and crocus hues,
And daffodils' yellow ascendancy.
Buds open into perfect winged green crowns.

Light's brief liquefaction of bright metal
Fixed to your yard of hair by its strong pin
Estranges sight's routine passivity
Between thick hedges bordering empty fields.
The well-wrought simple Corinthian beauty
Of this gift from Lesley's hand gave this donnée,
A token of art's power to transform
She would be pleased to know had lit from you.

But she left Hull this time last year, missing
Full Spring that waited in straining branch tips
Outside her window, the barque of her bed
Bearing her away, and last time we met
She was already faint with distance from the shore.
The bright stream of her spirits was not changed,
Her voyage occasioned no solemnity;
It was just the distance, the widening distance.

She had a pact with beauty, gave it rooms
To live in; light and space, colour and line,
Were affectionate *lares* in that house
Where she gave me the silver clasp for you.
Her voice's energetic lilt is gone
Since last I heard it reach me in a dream,
But light speaks her language of glad surprise
On the heliograph of this Grecian hair-clasp.

Report from up the Lane

Thin mist diminishes the distance
Of ancient mountains worn down to this
Uneventful land of drab green peace.
I scheme the theft of logs from the copse
Where sunlight on the boughs illumined
Verdigris of microscopic moss.

Near at hand the bare hedge is dripping
Its day-long dew onto the humped bank
Of grassed earth that curtails the garden,
Where she is digging the strawberry bed.
Wrists turning in the full spade's motion,
She makes her pact with the coming year.

When sleep's well is difficult to find,
Whether ghost or mood of mind or moon
Makes acute and troubles the darkness,
From beneath our eiderdowns we hear
Blown rain colliding with the window,
Crackling like random volleys of grit.

Years of this house might teach me its speech
Of faint wooden groans around midnight,
And by day isolation would hone
My curiosity to trade in
The local currency of rumour
In slow exchanges at the lane's end.

The twelfth month, and the world has run down
To the stasis of frost-stiffened fields.
I have taken up observation
Of the animals' dumb fortitude,
And note how the birds fly more slowly
Now the sky's sense of humour is dead.

The Rural Muse

Here there are all varieties of rain,
Some fine as mist, plenty of spattering drops,
Dense hedges that resent the hidden roads
That tortuously thread the countryside.
I am given facts of green, not ideas,
The alien silence of fields and sky
In the spaces between their background noise
Of the creatures and the leaf-rustling wind,
Or glum parables of stark containment,
Like several frogs trapped in the garden tank
Where a drowned mouse floats till all are tipped out.
No, it does not make me think, this valley,
Half way down which rain drums like hard boiling
On the thin roof of the lean-to kitchen.
Her green fist in my throat, the rural muse
Would have me believe that nature is enough.

Indigence

Rain has put an end to my work. I grub no more
In the nail-soiling earth deracinating weeds
In the large front gardens of the retired gentry,
But leap in the lane beneath the high hedges
That will soon supply me with berries and filberts,
For summer is surely ended, and, though I starve
This winter, my season of labour is over.
I will go on sleeping in the flimsy outhouse
I have occupied these seven years; shooting stars
Amuse me through its open end when August comes
With the Perseid showers scattering sky-silver.
I celebrate my improvidence by singing
A song about chickens I learned as a boy.
The wet wood on my fire hisses like steady rain.
It chars before it burns, then quickly goes to ash.
Not much heat here, nor is my straw unduly clean,
Renewed each week from the adjacent cowshed.
I grow old, and shall not last much longer at this,
Expecting no successor in this neighbourhood.

Waiting

It is all going to seed, tall grasses feathery
With loads that rise showing eddies of wind,
The small indigenous poppies' sectioned cups
That spill black grains in scientific palms.
The direction of this coming topple
Into the many cycles' end is winter,
When the hedge shall sleep curled in upon itself,
And the cold will humble all prolific lives.

The Plough's three-quarters round the Pole
Tonight, the stars' presence a sign of season,
After weeks hidden in earth's risen damp.
The cold had both feet through the door that night
We made the life that balloons your abdomen now,
Approaching a comely pendulousness
As you step from the bath whose vapour drifts downstairs.
For seasons are not long if we define them strictly,

Though this shall be a summer's child,
A birth-day pressing on us, as dead ancestors
Stake out the place in unaccustomed traffic
Shunting in the dogleg of the lane to pass
This rickety house, and shadowy movements
Later at the threshold of my sight.
I apologise for familial circumstances,
Pray in the kitchen, try to make them welcome.

Stones

Mother of echoes, stone sharpens birdsong
So cities ring louder than miles of grass
When the sky's redeeming voices sound among
Spaces choked hard with architecture's mass.

Ruined sites where history's solid codes
Of monolith and pillar remain stored
Hold also chips and grit on ancient roads
Minutely detailing all that stone records.

The floodlit rock looming above the bay,
A jar of pebbles or a diamond ring,
All put stone's variousness upon display
And preach the integrity its silence sings.

In limestone Auden saw '*a faultless love*
Or the life to come', relied for truth on stone
That crystallised as marble rises above
The impermanence for which art can atone.

Stone grinding grain, stone walls to live inside,
Or to keep back the tide that sifts the shingle,
Stones hold our days in place and will provide
Memorials when our bodies go to mingle

With the minerals whose surest form is stone,
The stuff of mountains, bedrock, our tough friend,
So ultimately our bones are not alone
Where stones will keep us company past the end.

On the Beach

Recall the near-drowning of your son
Through the deception of a pool's shelved floor,
And think your thanks beneath this clear blue sky
You were allowed the diving dash to save him.
Be grateful also, while the mountains' vast indifference
Inland and the miles of sea and sand force
A glad acceptance of powerless unimportance,
That the woman walking with you is beautiful
In this sun, and lovelier by the small light
Beside her bed, although she is not that son's mother,
And that he and his brother, whose presences
You imagine playing here, are always absent now,
And living, somewhere, where you cannot see them;
Dreams in which filial love inundates you,
The loss you feel when watching small boys' games,
Come like a rain to rust the bright metal of days
To uselessness, and what you call your heart
Can't tell what it wills, this present love or a time
When these sons may be wholly yours once more,
Who will always be yours either side of the grave.
But admit it is worth what the righteous call rejoicing
To be linked in a threesome with a woman who loves you
By her little daughter's hands. Without pretending
This child is yours, her happiness when mother's and your arms
Lift her to bear her through the air on your walk
Crosses the opened borders of your feelings
Like provisions a beleaguered people crave.
Believe your eyes that this is the world,
That the huge assuagement of the beach and the sea,
Their mild colours and unstrained continuity,
Can allegorise your life as satisfactorily
As the derelict structures in pathless forests
Posited for the poems that, thank God, you do not write.
In this air you barely remember the invidious need
For cigarettes where breathing itself is stimulating.
Examine what the child gives you, the razor fish
Smaller than any you've seen, almost too fragile
To touch with these fingers of yours, so its brittle arc
Instructs you in gentleness. Take it home,

With the iridescent chip of shell, the traces of sand
That will lodge a long time in the seams of your pockets,
And, now you have written these hours' memorial
In verse as easy as the walk you took,
Go back sometime to Ynyslas, with Karen and Little El.

Day In, Day Out

Fine days in early winter are clear light
Down all the valley's long intricacies,
A distance of the river's meandering
Where adjoining vales occlude its curving
To the sea beyond the last range of hills.

Inside I study different fires by night,
The hues of various woods' combustion
Or metallic yellow of soft coal's flames,
Effulgent landscapes of the ember hells
And thin smoke clouding in the varnished beams.

Another weekend comes over the hill.
Saturday is perpendicular rain,
Soaking the woodchips from my hatchet work,
Weighting the countless leaves and blades of green.
The morning's eggs steam, breath mists the table.

They are sitting beside the dying fire,
A man and wife speaking softly in Welsh.
Upstairs I lie afraid of these shadows,
Who sometimes move an object carefully,
Recalling their rights to the mantelpiece.

The two stone sheds sag under the weather,
Their mortar crumbling, their beams going soft
In the percussion of insistent rain,
Each full drop bursting like a glass grenade
On the packed black mud of the rough pathway.

I look for optimism in the night
While urinating onto the dark earth,
Aimlessly gazing for falling meteors
That vary the fixed plan of heaven's lights.
I wish for success, and shrug at the sky.

As there is no thread or pattern in it,
Let us spend the day on the hill, my love,
With a fine view of the rain on our house
Some distance between its neighbouring farms
In the wet fascination of winter.

Provision

The man employed to heave the trailers empty
Displays his strength unthinkingly on meat
Daydreaming obdurately of nothing
En route to sale and mechanical death.

With a tool for the job and routine haste
The subtle fabric of sheep's ears receives
Its issue of round thoroughfares of daylight
For tags by which the ledgers herd their beasts.

Heads shaken in the pens spray venous blood
Instantly absorbed in rain and excrement,
Darkest green, discharging its chlorophyll
Down echelons of gutters to the river.

Gravity likewise their guts' psychopomp,
From the lurching train of hooked carcasses
A chute permits the lolling yards to slide
To a skip where they brim like discarded blancmanges.

On Mondays all the butchers' blinds are down
Commemorating Sundays' pause in slaughter.
Inside the shops that smell of blood and sawdust
Stale bread is ground to give the faggots body,

Band-saws reduce the riven barrels of pigs
To cardboard boxfuls of deep-frozen chops.
Ripe for flies in a badly drained yard,
Six heads are on view in a clear plastic sack;

Lugged to the burning-pit in the meadow,
Their horns and closed eyelids describe firm arcs,
Become ulterior in bestial decorum,
Quietly stating everything is settled.

With the Offal Eaters
(for Sophie)

The offal eaters burn resinous wood
That causes black dust to stick to their hands
That have split the trunk sections and stacked them
To dry on the stones of the unclean hearth.
Winter, and much of their talk is of fuel,
Between the concentrated silences
Of each day's chronology of meal-times.

After beer, the oily taste of offal
Nudges the memories of their back teeth
That prefer the texture of wood pigeon,
Or even the mundane flesh of an egg.
In putting each beast killed to its full use
Their wives chop offal finely twice a week,
Serving it awash in salty gravy.

In the slow dying of their old habits
One keeps a toothbrush, one a fountain pen,
Sentimentally used from time to time,
As are razors, and even a steam iron.
Weather has quite replaced television
As focus of irrelevant interest.
They are specialists of all types of rain.

Clothes of unbleached wool and well-patched trousers
Soiled with the ochre of the local earth,
Boots scuffed to leaking tied with strips of hide,
Are piled on the floor after peasant disrobings
Precede the donning of maculate shifts.
In bed one curses offal to his wife,
Who curses him, and so they go to sleep.

Morning, and the year's first snow is falling
For infants perched on the broad windowsill.
Two men with saws address a thick pine trunk
While in the outhouse women flense the pig.
Plain appetites are ready for midday.
Scrubbed potatoes steam beside the salt pouch,
Offal crumbs in the trestled board's deep grain.

Douglas Houston was born in 1947 in Cardiff. He grew up in Scotland, and studied English at Hull University from 1966 to 1969, and then worked in Hull as a schoolteacher. After teaching English in Germany, he returned to Hull to work on a Ph.D. in modern poetry. In 1982 he moved back to Wales, and now lives near Aberystwyth.

Douglas Houston's poems have appeared in many magazines and anthologies, including Douglas Dunn's book *A Rumoured City: new poets from Hull* (Bloodaxe Books, 1982). *With the Offal Eaters* is his first collection of poems.